# TABLE OF C

*The*

# GODDESS

## TAROT

## WORKBOOK

# The GODDESS TAROT WORKBOOK

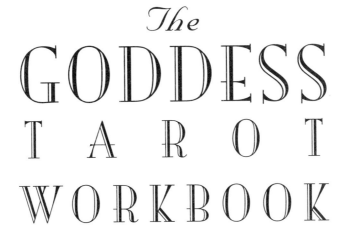

*by Kris Waldherr*

U.S. GAMES
SYSTEMS, INC

U.S. GAMES SYSTEMS INC.

*Other books by Kris Waldherr*

*Sacred Animals*

*The Book of Goddesses*

*Persephone and the Pomegranate*

↢ ↢ ↢

Art, design, and text by Kris Waldherr Art and Words
www.artandwords.com

Visit the Goddess Tarot website at
www.goddesstarot.com

ISBN 1-57281-285-0

00 10 9 8 7 6 5 4 3 2

Printed in Canada

U.S. Games Systems, Inc.
Stamford, CT 06902 USA

# INTRODUCTION

The *Goddess Tarot Workbook* is an invitation for you to personalize the Goddess Tarot for yourself. Think of this book as the ultimate private workshop where the main subject under consideration is you and your life alone. Here in this workbook you will find the space to explore your hopes, your dreams, your past, your future—in other words, your unique myth or story that no one else possesses.

Goddesses aren't the only women with myths of their own. Our lives all bear a story unlike anyone else's; as rich and individual as any divinity, as full of amazing wonders and surprises, disappointments and joys. This workbook has been created to aid you in revealing yours. Through this process you will know yourself better than you thought you did. You will also gain valuable tools to help you personalize your work with the Goddess Tarot, thus aiding you in becoming a more intuitive and empowered user of this unique form of goddess wisdom.

As you explore your personal myth within *The Goddess Tarot Workbook*, I hope this process will help you acknowledge your magic and strength. You are as individual and miraculous as any divine being ever worshipped through the ages.

## HOW TO USE THIS WORKBOOK ✧ ✧ ✧

*The Goddess Tarot Workbook* is set up as an interactive experience, one where you participate by using the vital fabric of your own experiences and beliefs. Though some of the areas covered in this workbook may not require having the cards at hand, it is meant to be used in partnership with the Goddess Tarot deck.

The materials offered here explore the individual cards of the Goddess Tarot. The workbook also provides six tarot spreads, each keyed to a particular life situation, which show ways to concretely use the tarot deck. As you leaf through this workbook, you will find a greater development of the information offered in *The Goddess Tarot* book. No doubt you will also notice that many of these pages contain thought-invoking questions for you to answer, special ruled areas for you to write your thoughts about the cards and to record your tarot readings. This is because this workbook is a *work book* in the truest sense; it was created to be completed by you in the very special and individual way that only you can offer.

One way to consider *The Goddess Tarot Workbook* is to think of it as a guided journal. As in the best and most personal journals, you will have the opportunity to delve into your deepest and dearest beliefs; you will record your most precious memories and emotions; you can write about your most private hopes for your brightest future.

The ideal way to use this workbook is to work with it over time using the seventy-eight cards of the Goddess Tarot deck. As you get to a page, take out the relevant card and gaze at it for a moment before you write your answers to the questions. Consider this act a type of waking dreaming—let your mind free associate and see what surprising answers may emerge. As well, take note of any feelings or memories that surface, any reactions you might have to the colors or symbols in the goddess art.

As you work through the individual cards and tarot spreads offered here, I hope they will jump start you into exploring the distinctly feminine issues presented by the Goddess Tarot. Many of the materials presented here are written to challenge your beliefs, and to offer you a glimpse of a more authentic life. Some of them may open up issues at which you'd rather not look, while others may have you bubbling over with optimism and energy.

You may find no easy answers here, but you will find something even more valuable— an opportunity to explore and record the multitude of riches contained within your life.

## ABOUT THE GODDESS TAROT ❧ ❧ ❧

I created The Goddess Tarot using a combination of art from my book *The Book of Goddesses* as well as original art specifically created for the deck. The Goddess Tarot draws inspiration from the many goddesses honored through history, using goddess myths and imagery to update traditional tarot symbolism. It acknowledges women's contemporary needs and mythic past and is meant as an easy-to-use, alternative deck for tarot readers already familiar with the popular Rider-Waite or Aquarian decks; for those who seek a deeper experience of the Divine Feminine in their readings. For newcomers to the tarot, I hope the inclusion of goddess myths and symbolism will add relevance and depth.

Like most tarot decks, the Goddess Tarot contains seventy-eight cards. These seventy-eight cards are divided into two arcanas, or mysteries. The word "arcana" is related to the word "arcane," meaning containing esoteric information—information available to those knowledgeable enough to understand the secret language of symbolism. So that secret knowledge may become wisdom shared, each card and its imagery are explained in greater depth within this workbook.

The major arcana explores the major archetypes and universal questions we all experience as we journey through life. In the minor arcana, the great themes explored in the major arcana are brought to earth, and made relevant to the individual experiences of our daily lives.

Besides representing an important aspect of life, each of the twenty-two major arcana cards of the Goddess Tarot are related to a goddess and her story. The art upon these cards presents the goddess as she is traditionally represented in her native culture. Each of these images are surrounded by a decorative border that depicts another aspect of her myth or power.

The fifty-six minor arcana cards of the Goddess Tarot are divided into four suits:

Can you give insight into ?

What do I need to understand about ?

What is the meaning of ?

What is the lesson or purpose of ?

How might I ?

How can I improve my chances of ?

ated to one of the four
ddess and her myth. Each
ties of the element with
v the path of wisdom that
nal satisfaction of Venus,
ative of Freyja, the Norse
ained through difficulties
tacles are offered to those
s of fortune.

ian as she undergoes the
oman" as an aspect of the
es all of us. Each number
—beginning with one, the
ition.

s, and queen) can reveal
f life: masculine, feminine,
t cards can also represent

O ~ BEGINNINGS

IARA

I ~ MAGIC

ISIS

II ~ WISDOM

SARASVATI

III ~ FERTILITY

ESTSANATLEHI

IV ~ POWER

FREYJA

V ~ TRADITION

JUNO

XXI ~ THE WORLD

GAIA

VI ~ LOVE

VENUS

XX ~ JUDGMENT

GWENHWYFAR

VII ~ MOVEMENT

RHIANNON

XIX ~ THE SUN

THE ZORYA

VIII ~ JUSTICE

ATHENA

XVIII ~ THE MOON

DIANA

IX ~ CONTEMPLATION

CHANG O

XVII ~ THE STAR

INANNA

X ~ FORTUNE

LAKSHMI

*Part One:*

# THE MAJOR ARCANA

XVI ~ OPPRESSION

THE WAWALAK

XV ~ TEMPTATION

NYAI LORO KIDUL

XIV ~ BALANCE

YEMANA

XIII ~ TRANSFORMATION

UKEMOCHI

XII ~ SACRIFICE

KUAN YIN

XI ~ STRENGTH

OYA

Many believe that the twenty-two cards of the major arcana tell a great story: the journey of humanity as they struggle to master progressive life lessons. In *The Goddess Tarot*, this story starts with the appropriately named card, Beginnings—affiliated with the Tibetan goddess Tara—and ends with the cumulative vision of The World—associated with the Greek earth goddess Gaia—with twenty cards and goddesses in between.

Some consider the tarot to hold all the world's wisdom distilled into images as potent in symbolism as any dream. But, as with a dream, the meanings ascribed to these cards should be made pertinent to your life experiences. Look upon these descriptions as a guide to spark your imagination and feelings. Also included are descriptions for reversed or upside-down cards. These can be used according to your judgment. I personally prefer to think of cards as being strong or weak by taking into consideration the question being asked, their relative position in a tarot spread and the cards surrounding it.

Often when major arcana cards show up in readings, they represent recurrent themes or important changes at hand. They promise more to a situation than meets the eye—challenging us to view our lives as larger than we can see, deeper than we can imagine.

### AN OVERVIEW OF THE MAJOR ARCANA ✧ ✧ ✧

| NUMERAL | MAJOR ARCANA CARD | GODDESS |
|---------|-------------------|---------|
| 0 | Beginnings | *Tara, Tibetan goddess of protection and compassion.* |
| I | Magic | *Isis, Egyptian fertility goddess.* |
| II | Wisdom | *Sarasvati, Hindu goddess of wisdom, education, and the arts.* |
| III | Fertility | *Estsanatlehi, Navajo goddess of the corn.* |
| IV | Power | *Freyja, Norse goddess of beauty and creativity.* |
| V | Tradition | *Juno, Roman ruling goddess.* |
| VI | Love | *Venus, Roman goddess of love.* |
| VII | Movement | *Rhiannon, Celtic horse goddess.* |

*[Handwritten annotations in left margin: Fool, Magician, High Priestess, Empress, Emperor, Hierophant, The Lovers, The Chariot]*

| NUMERAL | MAJOR ARCANA CARD | GODDESS |
|---------|-------------------|---------|
| VIII | Justice *Justice* | Athena, Greek goddess of wisdom. |
| IX | Contemplation *The Hermit* | Chang O, Chinese moon goddess. |
| X | Fortune *The Wheel of Fortune* | Lakshmi, Hindu goddess of fortune and prosperity. |
| XI | Strength *Strength* | Oya, Yoruba goddess of the Niger River and the winds. |
| XII | Sacrifice *The Hanged Man* | Kuan Yin, Chinese goddess of mercy. |
| XIII | Transformation *Death* | Ukemochi, Japanese food goddess. |
| XIV | Balance *Temperance* | Yemana, Santeria goddess of the Caribbean Sea. |
| XV | Temptation *The Devil* | Nyai Loro Kidul, Javanese goddess of the waters. |
| XVI | Oppression *The Tower* | The Wawalak, sister Australian Aboriginal fertility goddesses. |
| XVII | The Star *The Star* | Inanna, Sumerian goddess of the stars and heavens. |
| XVIII | The Moon *The Moon* | Diana, Roman goddess of the moon. |
| XIX | The Sun | The Zorya, a trio of Slavic guardian goddesses who attend the sun god. |
| XX | Judgment | Gwenhwyfar, Celtic sovereign goddess. |
| XXI | The World *Gaia* | Gaia, the Greek goddess who symbolizes the earth. |

# 0 ~ BEGINNINGS ~ Tara
## Traditional card: The Fool

**Keywords:** New ventures, trust, innocence

**Meanings:** Time for the start of a great, new journey. Innocence that allows one to be open to blessings. New beginnings. Optimism and trust. Feeling protected by divine forces.

**Reversed or weakly aspected:** A need to look deeper into an opportunity before proceeding. Overconfidence—leaping before looking. Folly or naivety.

✦ ✦ ✦

AFFILIATED WITH BEGINNINGS is the compassionate mother goddess Tara, who is perhaps the most important deity for Tibetan Buddhists. Endowed with the power to heal all sorrows and grant all wishes, she is honored as the protectress against the fears that block men and women from living in harmony. Stories about Tara reveal the worries that concerned the people of ancient Tibet: for example, she is reputed to protect her followers from the fear of elephants and snakes. But the most dangerous fears are often insidiously masked. These are the ones that can wreak the most damage to our self-confidence and peace of mind, keeping us from living as happily as we'd like.

Often our fears will emerge as we begin a new phase of life: a promising relationship, a new venture, a change of home or job. It is as if our desire for this change has given birth to an equally violent reaction which will not allow us to grow. The appearance of this card is an invitation for us to consider the functions these fears perform for us. Understanding them can be the first step toward releasing them.

*If I could start anything, what would I begin?* _____

_____

_____

*What fears are keeping me from starting this?* _____

_____

_____

_____

_____

_____

*This card reminds me of the following:* _____

_____

_____

_____

_____

_____

_____

_____

_____

*Other thoughts I have about this card:* _____

_____

_____

_____

_____

_____

_____

_____

_____

_____

_____

# I ~ MAGIC ~ Isis
## *Traditional card: The Magician*

**Associated with the Suit of Swords**
**Keywords**: Self-empowerment, awareness, mastery
*Meanings:* An awareness of the magic within yourself. A yearning to grow beyond limitations. The ability to transform your life through the strength of originality and personal power. Renewed creativity and vigor. Experiencing the Divine Feminine as a power within yourself.
*Reversed or weakly aspected:* Blocked power or creativity. Manipulating others. A need to control situations from behind the scenes. Secrecy.

✧ ✧ ✧

THE GREAT EGYPTIAN FERTILITY GODDESS ISIS, affiliated with Magic, is a potent symbol of alchemic transformation. For over 3000 years—from before 3000 B.C. to the second century A.D.—Isis was worshiped in Egypt as the great mother goddess of the universe. She was the sole possessor of the secret name of Ra, the Egyptian ruling god, which gave her unlimited magical powers. Using these powers, as well as the strength of her love, Isis was able to bring Osiris, her husband and brother, back to life for a short time after he was was murdered. Horus, the child she conceived of him during this interlude, grew to become one of the most powerful of the Egyptian gods.

This card suggests a growing awareness of the magic within yourself as well as a new yearning to grow beyond any limitations. You are able to transform your life through the strength of your originality and power—all you need to do is take possession of what you desire, much as Isis possessed the secret name of Ra.

*What does magic mean to me?*_____

_____

_____

_____

*What do I consider magical about myself?* _____

_____

_____

_____

_____

_____

*This card reminds me of the following:* _____

_____

_____

_____

_____

_____

_____

*Other thoughts I have about this card:* _____

_____

_____

_____

_____

_____

_____

_____

_____

# II ~ WISDOM ~ Sarasvati
## Traditional card: The High Priestess

**Keywords:** Spirituality, education, enlightenment

**Meanings:** An interest in spiritual knowledge. A teacher who will share with you what you are seeking—or perhaps you are that teacher. Wisdom gained in a graceful manner. Honoring the powers of intuition, dreams, the Divine Feminine.

**Reversed or weakly aspected:** Lack of trust in intuition. Over reliance on intellect. Superficial knowledge. Fear of searching within oneself for answers.

✤ ✤ ✤

SARASVATI, THE HINDU GODDESS OF KNOWLEDGE, is the divinely feminine embodiment of wisdom. Especially honored by scholars and musicians, Sarasvati is credited in India with creating the fruits of civilization: the first alphabet, the arts, mathematics and music. Sarasvati is easily recognizable by her dazzling white skin and brilliant clothing; this brightness represents the powerful, pure light of wisdom that destroys the darkness of ignorance. Her four arms symbolize how her influence extends over the four directions of the earth and, by extension, all areas of life. The book she holds in one of her hands represents education; the beads she holds in another hand indicate spiritual knowledge; with her other two hands she holds a *vina*, an Indian lute, representing the art of music, which can inspire thoughts of beauty.

The appearance of the Wisdom card offers a new phase of life from which much knowledge will be gained in a graceful manner. You may also be experiencing a growing interest in spiritual matters. This card suggests the discovery of new, soulful depths within yourself, or the meeting of a teacher who can help you access that part of yourself.

*Where would I like to gain more wisdom?*_____

_____

_____

*What can I do to encourage wisdom in my life?* _____

_____

_____

_____

_____

_____

*This card reminds me of the following:* _____

_____

_____

_____

_____

_____

_____

_____

*Other thoughts I have about this card:* _____

_____

_____

_____

_____

_____

_____

_____

_____

_____

# III ~ FERTILITY ~ Estsanatlehi
## Traditional card: The Empress

**Keywords:** Fecundity, abundance, growth

**Meanings:** Feelings of fertility and abundance. A new marriage or special relationship which celebrates one's growth as a woman. Creativity which manifests as physical product, whether that be children, artistic endeavors or wealth. A pregnancy, either of yourself or someone close to you.

**Reversed or weakly aspected:** The opportunity to work through the manure of the past to better fertilize your life. Deprivation or sterility. Feeling the lack of material resources.

✧ ✧ ✧

ASSOCIATED WITH FERTILITY, this benevolent Navajo corn goddess symbolizes the ever-changing, ever-fertile earth. Like the earth itself, Estsanatlehi appears as a young maiden during the spring and summer months. As the wheel of the year changes to fall and winter, she also changes to take on the features of a crone. For this reason, the goddess is also called Changing Woman. Estsanatlehi is honored as the creator of the Blessingway, a series of Navajo rituals. The ceremonies which make up the Blessingway are used for weddings, childbirth rites, and other joyous occasions in the life of the Navajo.

This card suggests you may be experiencing feelings of abundance and fertility as well as a renewed interest in sensuality. Your creativity may be manifesting itself in physical products: children, artistic endeavors or wealth. If you are feeling a lack of these things, perhaps even a sense of depravation, it is time to ask yourself where your life needs fertilizing. Working through the manure of the past can help grow a more fruitful future.

*What would I like to physically manifest in my life?* _____

_____

_____

_____

*What can I do to help this grow?* _____
_____
_____
_____
_____
_____
_____

*This card reminds me of the following:* _____
_____
_____
_____
_____
_____
_____
_____

*Other thoughts I have about this card:* _____
_____
_____
_____
_____
_____
_____
_____
_____
_____
_____

# IV ~ POWER ~ Freyja
## *Traditional card: The Emperor*

*Associated with the Suit of Staves*
*Keywords:* Leadership, wisdom, authority

*Meanings:* The ability to use power wisely. The awareness of one's power. Meeting an authority figure or teacher who can help. The ability to lead and inspire others. Knowledge of how to "work the system" without giving up personal values or resorting to violence or deception.

*Reversed or weakly aspected:* Oppressed by another's power and authority. Insecurity. Loss of personal power. Passive aggression. Manipulating others.

✦ ✦ ✦

FREYJA, THE NORSE GODDESS of creativity, love, and beauty, explores the issue of Power through her connection with the warring Aesir and the peaceful Vanir.

The Norse divided their gods and goddesses into two groups, the Vanir and the Aesir. Worshiped during the agricultural Bronze Age, the Vanir lived as one with the earth as they coaxed food from its fertile soil. Unfortunately, the Iron Age brought not only the first development of hunting tools and weapons; it also brought with it the combative Aesir, who declared war upon the Vanir. For the sake of peace, the Vanir agreed to give the Aesir their beloved goddess of beauty, Freyja. In this way, Freyja became the bridge between the old world—before iron tools—and the new, where power was often expressed with violence instead of diplomacy. Accordingly, she is associated with Power.

Freyja's myth offers the lesson that true power lies in the ability to choose between aggression and passivity at the right time. Often when we feel the need to express power we forget to consider the best way to do it; we react instead of observing objectively. Remember, the more powerful a person is, the less might they need to use.

*How do I usually express my power?* _____

_____

_____

*Where would I like to have more power in my life?*_____

_____

_____

_____

_____

_____

*This card reminds me of the following:* _____

_____

_____

_____

_____

_____

_____

_____

_____

*Other thoughts I have about this card:*_____

_____

_____

_____

_____

_____

_____

_____

_____

_____

_____

# V ~ TRADITION ~ Juno
## Traditional card: The Hierophant

**Keywords:** Structure, conformity, ritual

**Meanings:** Following established social structures and traditions. In love relationships, the desire for the declaration of intentions for the sake of security. Awareness of public image. Wanting to conform in order to gain society's or an authority figure's approval. Possible rigidity.

**Reversed or weakly aspected:** The need to throw out old social structures which may no longer be fulfilling your needs. Fear of unconventional ideas and ways of approach. Nonconformity. Questioning traditions.

☙ ❧ ☙

THE POWERFUL ROMAN GODDESS JUNO is affiliated with Tradition. Honored as the patroness of marriage and other traditional rites of passages, the goddess was believed to watch over and protect all women from their first to last breath. For this reason among others Roman women called their souls "juno" in honor of the goddess. To this day, many people consider the month of June, which still bears Juno's name, to be the most favorable times to marry. Another tradition sacred to Juno is the Matronalia festival, which is no longer observed. Every year, on the first of March, the matrons of Rome held this special festival to ask the goddess to bless their marriages and help them safely give birth to healthy babies.

The traditions expressed in Juno's ceremonies gave comfort to their practitioners. They also offered a sense of continuity as they passed from one generation to the next. However tradition for tradition's sake can empty any ritual of nourishment or power. To keep them meaningful, sometimes traditions need to be questioned and revitalized.

*What traditions or rituals do I honor?* _____

_____

_____

_____

*Which ones nourish me? Why?*_____

_____

_____

_____

_____

_____

*This card reminds me of the following:* _____

_____

_____

_____

_____

_____

_____

_____

_____

*Other thoughts I have about this card:*_____

_____

_____

_____

_____

_____

_____

_____

_____

_____

# VI ~ LOVE ~ Venus
## Traditional card: The Lovers

**Associated with the Suit of Cups**

**Keywords:** Harmony, passion, sexuality

**Meanings:** A renewed awareness of the nature of passionate love and what is needed to encourage it. Artistic creativity. Sexuality. The integration within oneself of the masculine and feminine, the god and the goddess—the Divine Marriage, if you will. A new, important relationship.

**Reversed or weakly aspected:** Manipulating others with sexuality. Inability to find a loving partner. Immaturity and irresponsibility in love relationships. Game playing. Disharmony.

⌁ ⌁ ⌁

VENUS, THE ROMAN GODDESS OF LOVE, brings joy to gods and humans as well as to the plant world. Not surprisingly, she is associated with the arrival of spring, that most love-inspiring of seasons. Created from the happy union of sea and sky, Venus has been described as "the queen of pleasure"; for it is this goddess who inspires people to enjoy the pleasures of sensuality and passion. However with these delights comes responsibility for another's happiness: the more one loves, the more open the lover is to the beloved, thus the more entwined and vulnerable hearts can become.

Often this card suggests a renewed awareness of the nature of passionate love and what is needed to encourage its growth. A new, important relationship may be on the horizon, one that dares you to live up to this challenge. It also offers the promise of artistic creativity, beauty and sexuality—as well as the ability to recognize the passionate bounty surrounding us in our lives.

*What would my ideal love relationship be like?* _____

_____

_____

_____

*Some ways I nurture my relationship with myself:*_____

_____

_____

_____

_____

_____

*This card reminds me of the following:* _____

_____

_____

_____

_____

_____

_____

_____

_____

*Other thoughts I have about this card:*_____

_____

_____

_____

_____

_____

_____

_____

_____

_____

_____

# VII ~ MOVEMENT ~ Rhiannon
## Traditional card: The Chariot

**Keywords:** Timing, transition, change

**Meanings:** Movement into the next phase of life. If you are feeling impatient, don't worry—transitions will go smoothly, as if you are being pulled by the twin forces of fate and fortune. External forces that work with you. Career advancement. Good timing!

**Reversed or weakly aspected:** Necessity of waiting. Impatience. Inconvenient timing. Disregard or insensitivity to the signs around yourself. Feeling trapped or unable to make a transition.

✣ ✣ ✣

THE BRITISH HORSE GODDESS RHIANNON is believed to appear to her followers riding an unearthly white horse. In this way, Rhiannon symbolizes the unceasing force of Movement that pulls all of life along with it. Rhiannon's name is derived from "rigantona," which means "great queen goddess." In an earlier period, she was known as Epona. Many ancient statues of her as Epona have been found, most of them depicting her with a mare on one side and a bundle of grain on the other. This image best symbolizes movement's eventual end: the great cumulation of harvest.

The appearance of Movement depicts a transition into a new phase of life. This card also often appears when there will be career advancement or fortunate timing. If you are feeling impatient, don't worry—all will be settled in its own time.

*Where would I like more movement in my life?* _____

_____

_____

_____

_____

*How do I think my life will change because of it?* _____

_____

_____

_____

_____

_____

*This card reminds me of the following:* _____

_____

_____

_____

_____

_____

_____

_____

*Other thoughts I have about this card:* _____

_____

_____

_____

_____

_____

_____

_____

_____

_____

# VIII ~ JUSTICE ~ Athena
## *Traditional card: Justice*

**Keywords:** Wisdom, detachment, fairness

**Meanings:** The need for a more detached viewpoint towards a troublesome situation. Imagine you are as wise as Athena and look at the situation. What should you do? Are you being fair to yourself and those around you? Worry not—you will be able to defend yourself; reasonable ears will hear and justice will be done.

**Reversed or weakly aspected:** Frustration with bureaucracies or organizations. Impatience with red tape. The appearance of this card shows that this is a temporary situation.

❧ ❧ ❧

ATHENA, THE GREEK GODDESS OF WISDOM, is associated with Justice. One of the most powerful of the ancient Greek goddesses, she is often depicted with an owl as a symbol of enlightenment and a serpent as a symbol of fertility. Athena's brilliance of reason was said to be as penetrating as her clear, gray eyes. Though her beauty brought her the attention of many, she chose to remain unattached, preferring the land of the intellect over the ocean of romantic entanglements. In time, Athena came to be revered not only as the goddess of wisdom, but also as the goddess of war. Though Athena was skilled without equal in the art of battle, she valued peace over discord and gave her protection to only those in need of defense.

This card often appears when there is a need to take a more detached viewpoint of a troublesome situation. Imagine yourself as wise as Athena and look at it anew. Is there a solution you may have overlooked? Alternately, Justice suggests frustration with bureaucracies or organizations, an impatience with snarled red tape. We all need to feel that the world is a fair place—the appearance of this card promises the exploration of this issue.

*What do I consider true justice?* _____

_____

_____

*Where do I feel injustice in my life?* _____

_____

_____

_____

_____

_____

*This card reminds me of the following:* _____

_____

_____

_____

_____

_____

_____

*Other thoughts I have about this card:* _____

_____

_____

_____

_____

_____

_____

_____

_____

_____

# IX ~ CONTEMPLATION ~ Chang O
## *Traditional card: The Hermit*

**Key words:** Meditation, withdrawal, introspection

**Meanings:** The need to go within to gain knowledge. Withdrawal to better contemplate life's direction. Retreat into inner life—at this time, your needs are not so focused on relationships with others, but on strengthening your relationship with yourself.

**Reversed or weakly aspected:** Distracting oneself by immersion in the world. Refusal to listen to intuition. No time to think or reflect. Superficiality.

✧ ✧ ✧

CHANG O, THE CHINESE MOON GODDESS, symbolizes the need for withdrawal from the world to better contemplate the universal questions of life.

Before Chang O became a moon goddess, she lived among the gods and goddesses with her husband, Yi, the Divine Archer. But when Yi shot nine suns out of the sky, leaving only one to warm the earth, the unlucky couple were stripped of their immortality and forced to live among humans. Chang O was dismayed and begged her husband to seek the potion of immortality from the goddess Hsi Wang Mu. Hsi Wang Mu was sympathetic, so she gave Yi enough for them to become immortal—but not enough for them to become divine once more. But Chang O had an idea. If she drank Yi's portion as well as her own, perhaps she would become a goddess again. After all, she reasoned, she was not the one who shot down the suns, so why should she be punished? Too tempted to resist, she drank it all. Soon Chang O felt herself become as light as ether as she floated away toward the heavens. Before she knew it, she was on the moon, once again a beautiful goddess—but unable to leave because of her weightlessness. There she spent eternity alone contemplating the separation between humanity and divinity.

Unlike Chang O we do not need to spend our entire lives separated from the world to receive the benefits of contemplation. The appearance of the Contemplation card suggests it is time to allow ourselves this luxury, so often overlooked and neglected. We all need time alone.

*If I had more time, what would I contemplate?* _____

_____

_____

_____

_____

*Some simple ways to gain time for myself:* _____

_____

_____

_____

_____

_____

_____

*This card reminds me of the following:* _____

_____

_____

_____

_____

*Other thoughts I have about this card:* _____

_____

_____

_____

_____

_____

_____

_____

_____

# X ~ FORTUNE ~ Lakshmi
## Traditional card: The Wheel of Fortune

**Associated with the Suit of Pentacles**

**Keywords:** Prosperity, expansion, chance

**Meanings:** The generosity of the universe. The ability to be open to abundance. Feelings of expansion and positive expectations. Awareness of beauty and love. Chance.

**Reversed or weakly aspected:** Uncomfortable feelings or disappointing experiences with chance. Unexpected endings or beginnings. Capriciousness.

✧✧✧

THE HINDU GODDESS of good fortune and prosperity, Lakshmi is believed to be attracted to sparkling jewels—so similar to the riches she bestows upon her loyal supplicants. In Hindu mythology, Lakshmi is believed to represent all that is feminine, while her consort, Vishnu, known as the Conqueror of Darkness, represents all that is masculine. Paintings from India often show Lakshmi and Vishnu riding on the back of Garuda, the giant king of birds, as they fly across the land spreading fortune. To woo her favor, every November on the night of the new moon Indian women clean their homes and hang tiny lanterns that glitter like diamonds in the darkness. Not surprisingly, many believe she lives in the sky with the stars, whose gem-like brilliance serves to adorn her beauty.

The Fortune card suggests that your consciousness is flying to embrace good fortune and abundance. You may also be experiencing a new awareness of the beauty and love around you. The universe can be an expansive, generous place. If you feel even the tiniest resistance to this idea, perhaps now is the time to examine the role that expectations play in creating our futures.

*What expectations do I have about fortune?* _____

_____

_____

*Why do I believe this?* _____

_____

_____

_____

_____

_____

*This card reminds me of the following:* _____

_____

_____

_____

_____

_____

_____

_____

*Other thoughts I have about this card:* _____

_____

_____

_____

_____

_____

_____

_____

_____

_____

_____

_____

# XI ~ STRENGTH ~ Oya
## Traditional card: Strength

*Keywords:* Courage, leadership, inner strength

*Meanings:* Any strength and any wisdom you need are within you now. Powers of speech to transform weakness into strength. Integrity and adherence to one's vision. The strength to create peace between opposing forces. These forces may be internalized or personified in a situation. Tame them—you have the strength!

*Reversed or weakly aspected:* The scattering of energies. Imbalance. Creating discord for the sake of sport. Valuing the lower energies over the higher.

✧ ✧ ✧

THE STORM GALES that Oya, the Nigerian goddess of the wind, creates are strong enough to tear the roofs off houses and uproot huge trees. Appropriately she is associated with Strength, a card of great integrity and power.

Since words are made of the wind we exhale when we breathe—and since Oya is praised for her eloquent speech—women often ask this regal goddess for the right words to ease conflicts and gain power. For this reason and others Oya is considered a powerful patroness of female strength and leadership. To please Oya, many Yoruba wear strings of maroon beads around their necks and keep altars in their homes displaying objects sacred to her: buffalo or "bush cow" horns, a copper crown symbolizing the copper palace where she lives, her favorite bean cakes.

Often we underestimate the power of our words, our ability to better our lives by simply speaking up. The appearance of this card reminds us that we inherently possess this talent as women—all we need to do is own it. If you are afraid to take charge by using this strength, consider what you fear may happen once you do.

*finding your voice*

*Where do I need more strength in my life?* _____

_____

_____

*What would happen if I expressed this strength?* _____

_____

_____

_____

_____

_____

_____

*This card reminds me of the following:* _____

_____

_____

_____

_____

_____

_____

_____

_____

*Other thoughts I have about this card:* _____

_____

_____

_____

_____

_____

_____

_____

_____

_____

_____

_____

# XII ~ SACRIFICE ~ Kuan Yin
## Traditional card: The Hanged Man

**Keywords:** Compassion, surrender, patience

**Meanings:** A surrender to higher principles, more spiritual goals. Self abnegation; to deny (something) to oneself. The ability to take care of others in a compassionate, nurturing way. Sacrifice in order to make sacred, to gain enlightenment. Empathy. Sensitivity.

**Reversed or weakly aspected:** Avoiding pain for gain. Lack of compassion. Focus on materialism at the cost of spirituality. Displacing fears unto others instead of taking responsibility.

❧ ❧ ❧

ASSOCIATED WITH SACRIFICE, Kuan Yin is one of the most beloved goddesses of China. She is honored to this day as the holy mother of compassion.

Upon her death Kuan Yin was brought to heaven, where her pure heart and merciful nature transformed her into a goddess. But instead of allowing herself to enjoy heaven's rewards, the goddess begged to be sent back to earth to help anyone in need—vowing never to leave until human suffering was vanquished forever. And so Kuan Yin sacrificed herself for the good of all. Because she personifies boundless compassion and kindness, devotees of Kuan Yin believe that even the act of speaking her name brings relief from pain. Some say that she walks among us still, looking after the many humans still in need of her care.

Often we are required to be as boundless as Kuan Yin as we sacrifice ourselves for a greater good. However there can be a danger that we will may find more satisfaction in martyrdom than in supporting what we believe. Remember that to sacrifice is to make sacred—not to suffer.

*What are my thoughts about sacrifice?* _____

_____

_____

*Where have I sacrificed myself in the past?*_____

_____

_____

_____

_____

_____

_____

*This card reminds me of the following:* _____

_____

_____

_____

_____

_____

_____

_____

_____

*Other thoughts I have about this card:*_____

_____

_____

_____

_____

_____

_____

_____

_____

_____

_____

_____

# XIII ~ TRANSFORMATION ~ Ukemochi
## *Traditional card: Death*

**Keywords:** Change, endings and beginnings

**Meanings:** Transformations. The need to allow something to die in order to create room for the new. Change which may feel painful at first, but is necessary. Creating life out of death, in order to nurture oneself or others.

**Reversed or weakly aspected:** Stagnation. Fear of change. Adherence to the status quo. Resisting transformation. The need to move in a new direction, but the inability to do so. Rigidity. Displacing fears onto others.

✦ ✦ ✦

AFTER HER DEATH, the body of the Japanese food goddess Ukemochi was transformed to supply food and other goods to nurture all of humanity. Her head turned into cows, who ran off to populate the earth, and grain sprouted from her forehead. Then rice plants grew from her belly, their seed scattering everywhere to start new plants. Finally, her eyebrows twisted into silkworms, whose threads wove into rainbow-colored silks to clothe the gods and goddesses, protecting them from the harsh elements. And so through Ukemochi's death, life was created—beginning a new cycle of continuance.

So often in western society, death is looked upon as an end instead of as a transformation. We see the cycle of life as a straight line that begins in possibility and ends in destruction. Considering this, it is not surprising that we often resist change to cling to the old at the expense of new growth. While personal transformation can be a disconcerting experience, the Transformation card offers us the hope that change can be for the best."

*What do I most want to transform in my life?* _____

_____

_____

_____

*What do I most fear transforming about myself?* _____

_____

_____

_____

_____

_____

_____

*This card reminds me of the following:* _____

_____

_____

_____

_____

_____

_____

_____

_____

*Other thoughts I have about this card:* _____

_____

_____

_____

_____

_____

_____

_____

_____

_____

_____

# XIV ~ BALANCE ~ Yemana
## *Traditional card: Temperance*

*Keywords:* Harmony, self-control, balance

*Meanings:* Experiencing—or seeking—a deep sense of harmony and union. Integration and moderation. Balance between the spiritual (symbolized by water) and the physical (symbolized by earth). Union of the conscious and unconscious forces of life.

*Reversed or weakly aspected:* Imbalance. Discomfort. Inability to find peace within or with others. Lack of moderation.

✦ ✦ ✦

YEMANA, A BEAUTIFUL AND POWERFUL SANTERIA GODDESS of the ocean, is associated with Balance. As the divine mother of the fourteen gods and goddesses who make up the Santeria religion's sacred pantheon, she occupies an exalted position and is honored as "Holy Queen Sea." Not surprisingly, Yemana is said to own all the riches of the ocean: seashells, pearls, oysters, coral reefs, as well as every creature within its fertile depths. As the goddess of water, Yemana is often called upon to provide rain, water that nurtures all of life. This water created from the sky represents the necessary balance between heaven and earth—a balance which brings harmony to all who are fortunate enough to experience it.

This card suggests a state of grace where there is a deep sense of harmony. A balance has been reached between the spiritual (symbolized by water) and the physical (symbolized by earth or sand) worlds. This peaceful state is often obtained only after much struggle and consideration. If you are feeling a lack of balance within yourself, perhaps all that's needed is to invite this force into your life.

*Where would I like more balance in my life?* _____

_____

_____

*Some ways I can create more balance:* _____

_____

_____

_____

_____

_____

*This card reminds me of the following:* _____

_____

_____

_____

_____

_____

_____

_____

*Other thoughts I have about this card:* _____

_____

_____

_____

_____

_____

_____

_____

_____

_____

_____

# XV ~ TEMPTATION ~ Nyai Loro Kidul
## Traditional card: The Devil

**Keywords:** Inner turmoil, illusion, obsession

**Meanings:** Tempted by forces one cannot control. Something deep and dark within the psyche is personified as temptation or addiction. Envy. Sensual desires. Gluttony. Experiencing the envy of others. Feeling a lack of control. The need to be controlling.

**Reversed or weakly aspected:** Freedom from temptation. Mastery over something previously controlling—a habit, a person or a wound from the past. Transforming a weakness into a strength. The acceptance of one's darker or shadow side.

✧ ✧ ✧

NYAI LORO KIDUL, A SEDUCTIVE MERMAID GODDESS, is associated with Temptation. She symbolizes the mysterious hidden forces of the ocean—forces whose powers must be respected. In Java, where Nyai Loro Kidul is still honored, many know better than to swim in the waters where she rules. It is believed that she searches there for mortals to serve in her undersea realm. To appease the goddess, people leave offerings of coconuts, clothes and even fingernail clippings by the ocean's edge—all of which are eagerly accepted by the green sea's swirling waters.

Nyai Loro Kidul's elusive powers reflect the temptation of illusion, of beauties which enslave rather than enrich, of uncontrollable desires and passions. Every one has a dark side within themselves that can turn them from their highest purpose, what Jung would call the shadow. Many of us ignore our shadow, hoping it will simply go away. Instead we may find our shadow appearing where we least expect it: in the form of a person who bothers us, an addiction that enslaves us, a darkness we will not own. The appearance of this card invites us to own our weaknesses—and grow stronger despite them.

*What tempts me the most in my life?* _____

_____

_____

*What does this reveal about myself?*_____

_____

_____

_____

_____

_____

*This card reminds me of the following:* _____

_____

_____

_____

_____

_____

_____

_____

*Other thoughts I have about this card:*_____

_____

_____

_____

_____

_____

_____

_____

_____

_____

# XVI ~ OPPRESSION ~ The Wawalak
## Traditional card: The Tower

**Keywords:** Confusion, difficulties, release

**Meanings:** Feeling overwhelmed or oppressed by circumstances or emotions. Depression. Like the Wawalak, the "light" has left your life; you are waiting to be released from the darkness. A new start after a painful ending that may have shattered your view of the world. A pause before moving into a new phase of life.

**Reversed or weakly aspected:** Though your situation may feel overwhelming and intimidating, hidden forces are at work to transform things for the better. Be patient and trusting.

✧ ✧ ✧

As BOTH GODDESSES AND MOTHERS, the Wawalak symbolize the unending force of life in all women—a force that can never be oppressed for long. Accordingly they are associated with Oppression.

During the Dreamtime, a mythic period when gods and goddess still walked the earth, the Wawalak, a pair of Australian aboriginal sister goddesses, accidentally polluted the sacred waterhole of the Great Rainbow Serpent with a single drop of menstrual blood. Rains poured down in angry response and the waterhole flooded. The two sisters sang, hoping to appease the serpent as well as to protect their newborn babies. But the serpent emerged from the waterhole and swallowed the sisters and their infants in a huge gulp. Oppressed by darkness, fear and guilt, the Wawalak wept within the belly of the serpent—until they were reborn from it's mouth back into the light.

Often we feel as oppressed as the Wawalak must have been inside the Great Rainbow Serpent. It is difficult to imagine life improving—all we can see is never ending darkness. The appearance of this card suggests that while this situation is painful, it will not last.

*Where do I feel the most oppressed in my life?* _____

_____

_____

*What has caused this oppression?* _____

_____

_____

_____

_____

_____

*This card reminds me of the following:* _____

_____

_____

_____

_____

_____

_____

_____

_____

*Other thoughts I have about this card:* _____

_____

_____

_____

_____

_____

_____

_____

_____

_____

_____

_____

# XVII ~ THE STAR ~ Inanna
## *Traditional card: The Star*

**Keywords:** Inspiration, hope, dreams

**Meanings:** Awareness of goals and dreams. The self-respect and strength to follow them. Success, good fortune, creativity. All is well with the world; your highest hopes are supported by the universe. Follow your dreams without fear or censure—don't be afraid to work to make them happen!

**Reversed or weakly aspected:** Not following your bliss. Insecurity. Feelings of unworthiness. Not listening to intuition. Fear of following your dreams or reaching a goal.

✧ ✧ ✧

INANNA, THE GREAT GODDESS OF THE BRONZE AGE, was said to be clothed with the stars, with the zodiac wrapped around her waist as a celestial girdle. In Sumeria, where she was worshiped five thousand years ago, Inanna was honored as the queen of heaven; appropriately, her temple was called Eanna or "house of heaven." Besides ruling over the heavens, Inanna was credited with power over the most important aspects of Sumerian life. Because they believed that all moisture was caused by the moon, Inanna was also the goddess of the rain clouds, necessary to that arid land where little water was available for growing grain.

Inanna is affiliated here with The Star. Besides affirming that all is well with your world, The Star is a reminder to follow your dreams without fear or censure. So often we wait for external signs of support before we allow ourselves to reach for what we most want. This card reminds us we are supported in more ways than we realize. With work we are fully capable of bringing our dreams into life.

*What do I most dream of creating?*_____

_____

_____

_____

*Other dreams I aspire to make real:*_____

_____

_____

_____

_____

_____

*This card reminds me of the following:* _____

_____

_____

_____

_____

_____

_____

_____

*Other thoughts I have about this card:*_____

_____

_____

_____

_____

_____

_____

_____

_____

_____

_____

# XVIII ~ THE MOON ~ Diana
## Traditional card: The Moon

**Keywords:** Femininity, intuition, emotion

**Meanings:** The receptive, nurturing aspects of the Divine Feminine. Intense emotions. Vivid or lucid dreams. Intuition. An opportunity to work on your relationship with that which truly nurtures you. The support of caring women.

**Reversed or weakly aspected:** Discomforted by emotional situations. Uneasiness with intuition, maternal figures, women. Feeling as changeable as the moon—instead of seeing this as a negative, recognize that what is empty will become full again in time.

✢ ✢ ✢

IN ANCIENT ROME, the goddess Diana was believed to rule over wild animals, hunting, and the moon. As the goddess of hunting Diana symbolized the Divine Feminine's ability to provide nurturing for all of its great and small creatures, even in the darkest winter when little grows. As the goddess of the moon, she ruled over that celestial body whose light was believed to influence the growth of crops and the pregnancy of women. The changing moon reflects the cycles of nature, for its light influences all growing things—humans, animals and plant—for better and for worse. The story of Diana reminds us of our connection to these cycles and that, like the moon itself, what is empty will become full if we are patient.

The Moon suggests intense emotions are as changeable as that beautiful orb. Instead of seeing this as a negative, recognize that what is empty will become full again—just as the moon does. These times can be seen as opportunities to work on your relationship with what truly nourishes you, to develop intuition and learn to trust yourself. You may also feel more aware of the nurturing of women who truly care about you.

*What situations or people nurture me the most?* _____

_____

_____

*What situations or things nurture me the least?*_____

_____

_____

_____

_____

_____

*This card reminds me of the following:* _____

_____

_____

_____

_____

_____

_____

_____

*Other thoughts I have about this card:*_____

_____

_____

_____

_____

_____

_____

_____

_____

_____

# XIX ~ THE SUN ~ The Zorya
## *Traditional card: The Sun*

**Keywords:** Creativity, success, fertility

**Meanings:** An expansive, life-affirming energy that brings opportunities and optimism. Creativity and inspiration. Relationships with children. Procreation. Love and sexuality. Masculine or yang, energy.

***Reversed or weakly aspected:*** Unwillingness to accept affection. Problems with children. Creativity blocked by external or internal forces. Delays in expanding unto the next phase of a project. Feeling thwarted.

✦ ✦ ✦

IN SLAVIC MYTHOLOGY, the Zorya are a trinity of sister goddesses who attend to the sun god, whose chariot rides through the sky every day to bring warmth to the earth. As well as attending to the sun god, without whose light all living things would perish, the Zorya are believed to be the guardians of the universe. As such, they stand watch over a fierce doomsday hound subdued by only a chained leash; one legend states that if ever this chain were to break, the end of the world would be at hand.

The Sun represents the brilliance of this life force that the Zorya protect—the incisiveness of intellect, the inspiration of creativity, the light that nourishes all life. Just as the sun shares its light, we all have special talents and qualities we should share with the world. The appearance of this card is a wonderful affirmation of this brilliant expansive energy—prepare to shine your light to the world. If you are uncertain what talents you have to offer, remember everyone has some special gift. It is time to own yours and offer it to the world.

*What special brilliance do I own?* _____

_____

_____

_____

*How can I share it with the world?*_____

_____

_____

_____

_____

_____

*This card reminds me of the following:* _____

_____

_____

_____

_____

_____

_____

_____

_____

*Other thoughts I have about this card:*_____

_____

_____

_____

_____

_____

_____

_____

_____

_____

_____

# XX ~ JUDGMENT ~ Gwenhwyfar
## *Traditional card: Judgment*

**Keywords:** Sovereignty, decisions, confidence

**Meanings:** Important decisions or news. Movement into the next phase of life. Time for a major and necessary change in life—often welcome, but frightening because of its magnitude. The confidence of a queen. Self knowledge.

**Reversed or weakly aspected:** Stagnation. Inability to act. Blockage. Giving up authority rather than living up to one's potential.

✧ ✧ ✧

GWENHWYFAR, THE WELSH GODDESS and first lady of the islands and sea, is believed to have existed as long as there has been surf to pound against rocky shore. Praised for her judgment and wisdom, it was prophesied that no man could rule Wales without her by his side. It is little wonder that many would-be kings attempted to abduct the once and future queen, since they foolishly thought that possessing her would make them king. They did not understand that it was Gwenhwyfar's judgment which made them sovereign, not some romantic entanglement.

The Judgment card presents an invitation for you to become queen of your life—to rule over your personal realm just as Gwenhwyfar ruled over Wales. It is a challenge for you to live as though you are, as intimidating as this may be. This card frequently appears when it is time for a major and necessary change in life —often welcome, but frightening because of its magnitude. See this card as an affirmation of your judgment; make your move with the confidence of a queen.

*If I were queen of my life, how would it change?* _____

_____

_____

_____

*How can I make these changes happen?* _____

_____

_____

_____

_____

_____

*This card reminds me of the following:* _____

_____

_____

_____

_____

_____

_____

_____

*Other thoughts I have about this card:* _____

_____

_____

_____

_____

_____

_____

_____

_____

_____

# XXI ~ THE WORLD ~ Gaia
## Traditional card: The World

**Keywords:** Expansion, travel, interconnection

**Meanings:** A new sense of expansion and hope. Experiencing connection with the universe, the source which nurtures us all. Travel and communications. Career growth. Hope. An awareness of the fragile ecological balance for which we are all responsible as residents of the earth. The Divine Feminine in action.

**Reversed or weakly aspected:** Fear of expansion. Feeling pessimistic about the future; even if you're uncertain how it will manifest, you are moving into a more hopeful period of life.

↬ ↬ ↬

FOR THOUSANDS OF YEARS and in cultures all around the world, the earth has been worshiped in one form or another. In ancient Greece, the earth was personified as a mysterious goddess called Gaia who was thought to have existed before all other life and to have created all of life. The myth of Gaia reminds us of the interconnection of all of the world, and the importance of living in harmony with its resources as well as among our fellow humans. To experience this harmony in our lives is perhaps the greatest gift of all.

The World symbolizes the interconnection and delicate balance of all of these forces. The appearance of this card suggests an experience of oneness with the universe as well as a new sense of expansion and hope. Inspiration and desire for positive change are also hallmarks of this card. Travel and communications may be featured, and career expansions for the better. All are ways to connect with the peoples and lands that make up the world.

*How do I see myself in the world?*_____

_____

_____

_____

*Where would I like to travel to in the world?* _____

_____

_____

_____

_____

_____

_____

_____

*This card reminds me of the following:* _____

_____

_____

_____

_____

_____

_____

_____

_____

_____

*Other thoughts I have about this card:* _____

_____

_____

_____

_____

_____

_____

_____

_____

_____

_____

_____

ACE

CUPS

TWO

CUPS

THREE

CUPS

FOUR

CUPS

QUEEN

CUPS

FIVE

CUPS

KING

CUPS

# Part Two:
# THE MINOR ARCANA

## The Suit of Cups

SIX

CUPS

PRINCESS

CUPS

SEVEN

CUPS

PRINCE

CUPS

TEN

CUPS

NINE

CUPS

EIGHT

CUPS

## *Element: Water, the moon*
## *Corresponds to Love, Major Arcana card number 6*

The suit of cups is associated with Venus, the Roman goddess of love and beauty. Cups symbolize the receptive aspect of the Divine Feminine: think of the Holy Grail whose mystical contents nurture spirit and flesh; think of a woman's womb whose fertile waters bring new life from the void. It is from the suit of cups that everything begins. Without the ability to be receptive to inspiration nothing can come into being—relationships, creative projects or spiritual enlightenment.

The cups proffered by Venus are an invitation to drink deeply of the magical water of love, life, inspiration, and pleasure at its purest. They offer us our first experience of the Divine Feminine at her most potent.

The appearance of cards bearing cups in a tarot reading suggests we are exploring an internal dreamscape: the mysterious world of emotions and artistic inspiration. To enter into this world is to embrace the natural fecundity of the Divine Feminine.

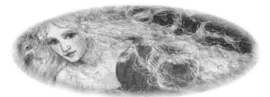

### THE MYTH OF VENUS ✤ ✤ ✤

Conceived and born of fertile sea, Venus is the bringer of joy, for it is love that begins all creation by inspiring us with thoughts of beauty and passion. For this reason, humans have beseeched Venus to favor their romances and creative artists have turned to Venus for inspiration. Shakespeare wrote a rather scandalous poem about her passionate relationship with Adonis; the painter Botticelli created one of the most sublime images in Western art when he depicted her ethereal birth from sea foam and water.

Often described as "the queen of pleasure," Venus was first worshiped as a nature goddess associated with the arrival of spring, only later gaining notoriety for her sensual exploits. In ancient Rome the goddess was honored every April first at the Veneralia, a festival to celebrate the arrival of Spring. No doubt in acknowledgement of the goddess's original function in their society, Ovid wrote that during the Veneralia all statues of Venus should be given "roses and other flowers; and then, as the goddess commands, you must wash yourself under the green myrhh."

Perhaps because she craved passion and love as much as she inspired it, Venus' romantic life was as complicated as some of the ones she blessed. While married to Vulcan, the lame god of the forge, she was also involved with Mars, the god of war. But it was with a mortal man, Anchises, that she gave birth to Aeneas, the hero of *The Aeneid*. Aeneas was a Trojan prince who escaped after the fall of Troy and sailed to Italy, where he founded the Roman Empire; and so through her son, Venus came to be considered the mother of the Roman people.

An Overview of the Suit of Cups, the Path of Venus ᧞ ᧞ ᧞

| MINOR ARCANA CARD | KEY WORDS |
|---|---|
| Ace of Cups | *the Divine Feminine, love, creativity* |
| Two of Cups | *harmony, partnership, love* |
| Three of Cups | *celebration, joy, harmony* |
| Four of Cups | *dissatisfaction, over-indulgence, boredom* |
| Five of Cups | *disappointment, sadness, pessimism* |
| Six of Cups | *memories, nostalgia, children* |
| Seven of Cups | *choices, indecisiveness, fantasy* |
| Eight of Cups | *leavetakings, disillusionment* |
| Nine of Cups | *the granting of wishes, sensuality* |
| Ten of Cups | *joyful closure, abundance, happiness* |
| Prince of Cups | *gentleness, intuition, an invitation* |
| Princess of Cups | *inspiration, grace, pleasure* |
| King of Cups | *practical artistry, mastery, creative control* |
| Queen of Cups | *soulfulness, emotion, inspiration* |

# ACE OF CUPS

**Keywords:** The Divine Feminine, love, creativity

**Meanings:** The Divine Feminine. The beginning of a new cycle ripe with potential and happiness. Great happiness. Start of a new love or friendship that will be important and emotionally nurturing. Creative inspiration and receptivity—a visitation from the Muses.

**Reversed or weakly aspected:** Emotional disappointment. Creative blockages. Disillusionment with love. Sadness or melancholy. Too much internalization of emotions.

✧ ✧ ✧

HERE, THE FULL MOON is contained, but not captured, within a single golden cup surrounded by the ocean, source of all life. Engraved upon this ornate goblet are ancient symbols of the Divine Feminine. Among these are the ancient triangle known as the *delphos*, whose womb-like shape celebrates the great trinity of earth, sea, and sky as well as the three stages of women; within this *delphos* is the glyph for Venus, the Roman goddess of love, who was born of sea. The light from the moon illuminates our most deeply held yearnings for pleasure, love, and emotional satisfaction. Water overflows from the cup, suggesting the richness of our emotions—they are so full of hope that they are literally spilling over in anticipation and celebration.

The Ace of Cups is a reminder of the inspiration we all hold within ourselves. It is an invitation for us to be receptive to our natural creativity, to let it speak through us.

*How can I be more receptive to inspiration?* _____

_____

_____

_____

_____

*Some projects for which I would like inspiration:* _____

_____

_____

_____

_____

_____

_____

*This card reminds me of the following:* _____

_____

_____

_____

_____

_____

_____

_____

*Other thoughts I have about this card:* _____

_____

_____

_____

_____

_____

_____

_____

_____

_____

_____

# TWO OF CUPS

*Keywords:* Harmony, partnership, love

*Meanings:* Harmony. Love. Enchantment. The integration of masculine and feminine aspects within oneself. An attraction that may become an important friendship or love relationship.

*Reversed or weakly aspected:* Infatuation. Disillusionment in a love relationship or intimate friendship. Overindulging in sensuality for the sake of the emotional "high."

⊱ ⊱ ⊱

IN A MYSTERIOUS MOONLIT GARDEN, the woman and her beloved pledge their faith with two golden cups. The woman, dressed in veils and robes of white, looks like the moon come down to earth. Inspired and made beautiful by love, she embodies the Divine Feminine to her lover; she is as enchanting as Venus, whose beauty inspires humanity to thoughts of harmony, love, and pleasure. Her lover, intoxicated by the possibilities that this woman represents, is healed by honoring her as his equal and opposite. Together they celebrate the divine marriage of the feminine to the masculine.

The appearance of the Two of Cups suggests the alchemic possibilities that a nurturing partnership can offer us. This partnership can be with another person or with a creative project. It can also be personified within ourselves as the integration of our masculine and feminine aspects. In whatever form it is expressed, all relationships present us with opportunities for love and healing.

*What is important to me in a partnership?*_____

_____

_____

_____

_____

*Describe a harmonious partnership:* _____

_____

_____

_____

_____

_____

_____

*This card reminds me of the following:* _____

_____

_____

_____

_____

_____

_____

_____

_____

*Other thoughts I have about this card:* _____

_____

_____

_____

_____

_____

_____

_____

_____

_____

_____

_____

# THREE OF CUPS

*Keywords:* Celebration, joy, harmony

*Meanings:* Great satisfaction. A reason to celebrate. Peace between family generations. A celebration involving women. Possibly a wedding feast.

*Reversed or weakly aspected:* Overindulgence. Procrastination. Distracting oneself with pleasure. Too much partying—time to get to work!

✦ ✦ ✦

THE WOMAN DANCES with two other women in a circle, one older than her, the other younger. They represent the three stages of woman—maid, mother, crone—that comprise the circle of life. Together they raise three cups in celebration. The wine intoxicates them, bringing warmth to their emotions and inspiration to their souls. The crone, in the fullness of life, raises her cup of knowledge and shares her wisdom with the woman. The youngest woman, the maiden, invigorates with her youthful energy and new ideas. The woman, centered between the two in the middle of her life's journey, feels satisfaction and pleasure as they dance. These three dancing women symbolize all of life's joys, potentials, and riches—all sacred to the goddess Venus.

The Three of Cups offers the promise of pleasure of a richly deserved celebration. So often joys are lost as we focus upon responsibilities and problems. The appearance of this card is a reminder that we are meant to be happy.

*What makes me happiest in my life?* _____

_____

_____

_____

*Description of the best celebration I ever attended:* _____

_____

_____

_____

_____

_____

_____

*This card reminds me of the following?* _____

_____

_____

_____

_____

_____

_____

_____

*Other thoughts I have about this card:* _____

_____

_____

_____

_____

_____

_____

_____

_____

_____

_____

# FOUR OF CUPS

**Keywords:** Dissatisfaction, over-indulgence, boredom

**Meanings:** Too much of a good thing. Taking something for granted—love, talents, beauty. Discontent. Need for re-evaluation of a relationship. Narcissism.

***Reversed or weakly aspected:*** Acceptance of the situation, though discontent is still present. A passing phase.

✧ ✧ ✧

AFTER OVERINDULGING IN TOO MANY PLEASURES, the woman sits beneath a tree with her eyes closed, hoping to ground herself after the excitement of intoxication. Behind her is the sea, symbolizing the watery nature of emotions, and a distant landscape—all that she no longer feels connected to. Four cups rest before her still offering their magical water but she has drunk too much; they no longer bear any attraction for her. A waning sickle moon mirrors the emptiness she feels.

The Four of Cups reveals the ennui that arrives with complacency. Often when we are given too much of a good thing we begin to take it for granted. As well, overindulgence can bring a sickening sense of dissatisfaction, for we have lost the distance necessary to appreciate the riches before us. The challenge inherent in this card is to find ways to see the bounty of our lives anew.

*Where do I feel bored in my life?* _____

_____

_____

_____

_____

*What do I do when I feel dissatisfied?* _____

_____

_____

_____

_____

_____

_____

*This card reminds me of the following:* _____

_____

_____

_____

_____

_____

_____

_____

_____

*Other thoughts I have about this card:* _____

_____

_____

_____

_____

_____

_____

_____

_____

_____

_____

_____

# FIVE OF CUPS

*Keywords:* Disappointment, sadness, pessimism

*Meanings:* Disappointment or disillusionment with relationships. Concentrating on problems instead of assets. Desire to move on. Creative blockage or infertility. Pessimism or depression.

*Reversed or weakly aspected*: A growing awareness that relationships are what you make of them. The ability to appreciate what one has—to drink of the two cups remaining if you will.

✧ ✧ ✧

NIGHT HAS FALLEN upon a desolate landscape decorated with five golden cups. Three of these cups have tipped over, spilling their magical water upon arid rocks. Disappointed, the woman, who is dressed in dark robes of mourning, leaves them behind to search for something better. But despite her pessimism, all is not lost—a few stars twinkle with hope at the horizon. However the moonless night is so dark that the woman cannot see them. Nor can she see the promise of Venus offered by the two cups still standing upright beside her.

The Five of Cups represents the disillusionment that often occurs in a relationship after the excitement of attraction begins to wane. This disappointment is part of the cycle of intimacy: as we get closer to another, we sometimes see more than we'd like. It is a natural reaction to mourn the idyllic euphoria of the start of a relationship.

*When have I felt disappointment in a relationship?* _____

_____

_____

_____

_____

*How did I deal with it?* _____

_____

_____

_____

_____

_____

_____

*This card reminds me of the following:* _____

_____

_____

_____

_____

_____

_____

_____

_____

*Other thoughts I have about this card:* _____

_____

_____

_____

_____

_____

_____

_____

_____

_____

_____

_____

# SIX OF CUPS

**Keywords:** Memories, nostalgia, children

**Meanings:** Harmonious home. Nostalgia. Children and childhood memories. Longing for the sweetness of the past, and its innocence. The ability to create sweetness within the home, incorporating the strengths of the past into the present.

**Reversed or weakly aspected:** Need to examine the past, including perhaps painful memories. The key to understanding may be locked there.

✤ ✤ ✤

IN A DREAM, THE WOMAN SEES THE TIDE RISE around six generously proportioned cups. Pulled by the moon's gravity, salt water floods around three cups. The remaining three rest upon an entry way to a thatched cottage filled with memories from the past. These cups are filled with wisteria as an offering to Venus, who brings forth flowers from the earth, and symbolize the rejuvenative aspects of the Divine Feminine.

The Six of Cups appears as a reminder of the sweetness of life. This sweetness can take on the form of nostalgia—a remembrance of some harmonious moment from our childhood, a time when the world may have seemed full of potential. Often the presence of children can bring up these memories anew. As we gaze upon them playing, we are reminded of our younger selves. For those with more troubled memories of youth, this card can be a painful reminder of all that happened to us when we were small and powerless. Whether sweet or sour, these potent emotions are an invitation to confront our past and create a richer present.

*What happy memories do I have of my childhood?*_____

_____

_____

_____

*Ways I feel strengthened by my past:*_____

_____

_____

_____

_____

_____

_____

*This card reminds me of the following:* _____

_____

_____

_____

_____

_____

_____

_____

_____

_____

*Other thoughts I have about this card:*_____

_____

_____

_____

_____

_____

_____

_____

_____

_____

_____

_____

# SEVEN OF CUPS

*Keywords:* Choices, indecisiveness, fantasy

*Meanings:* Overindulging in thoughts of what the future may bring. Daydreams. A choice is needed, a decision made in order to move forward and rejoin the world.

*Reversed or weakly aspected:* Allowing fantasies to influence how you view life—time to be more realistic. Projecting onto others instead of seeing things as they truly are.

↝ ↝ ↝

SURROUNDED BY SEVEN GOLD CUPS, the woman tries to choose but is unable to do so. These cups contain symbols of possible futures: the rose symbolizes the pleasures of Venus; the jeweled crown of earthly success; the laurels of victory; a castle; the snake of rejuvenation; and finally, a skull represents death and the afterlife. A cloth covers the mysterious contents of the seventh cup which contains the unknown. Surrounded by so many possibilities, the woman's eyes are closed, suggesting the desire to look within—or the need to wake up from fantastic dreams.

Daydreams are necessary to keep our lives full of potential and hope: if we can't imagine a future, we can't create it. But the Seven of Cups presents a challenge: it is time for us to take the wispy materials of our fantasies and transform them into reality. Often the more outlandish aspects of our daydreams will dissolve when considered under the light of day. This is to be expected and even encouraged. The dreams left behind will only be strengthened by this process.

*What is my favorite daydream or fantasy?* _____

_____

_____

_____

*Is there a way I can make it happen? How?* _____

_____

_____

_____

_____

_____

_____

*This card reminds me of the following:* _____

_____

_____

_____

_____

_____

_____

_____

_____

*Other thoughts I have about this card:* _____

_____

_____

_____

_____

_____

_____

_____

_____

_____

# EIGHT OF CUPS

*Keywords:* Taking leave of someone or something, disillusionment

*Meanings:* Time to move on. Need for more substance in life—whether that be more satisfying relationships, a more authentic way of life. Leavetakings.

*Reversed or weakly aspected:* Lingering too long in a difficult or superficial situation. Uncertainty about a relationship, whether to stay or leave. Doubts.

✧ ✧ ✧

IN AN EMPTY, ALMOST LUNAR-LIKE LANDSCAPE, the tide has retreated. A waning moon is just a sliver of light in a dark starless night. Within this mysterious setting, the woman walks away from eight cups from which she drank; she is searching for more substantial fare to feed her spirit. Though she knows the eight cups are empty she looks back, questioning her actions, hoping her decision to move on is correct. She wonders if she will ever again feel the pleasure and love represented by the goddess Venus.

The Eight of Cups offers us a difficult truth: in every relationship, no matter how sustaining it may have been, there comes a time when we need to grow. Often there is much pain in the recognition of this truth. The status quo is always comfortable even if it doesn't fulfill us as as it once did. But the nature of life is change: either our relationships must grow with us or they will die. These relationship changes can appear in many ways: the perfect job by which we are no longer satisfied, the old friendship that no longer nurtures us. The challenge is to either reinvent the relationship or to let go of it—the world is bountiful enough to fulfill our needs in new ways.

*What relationships no longer nurture me?* _____

_____

_____

*How can I transform them for the better?* _____

_____

_____

_____

_____

_____

*This card reminds me of the following:* _____

_____

_____

_____

_____

_____

_____

_____

*Other thoughts I have about this card:* _____

_____

_____

_____

_____

_____

_____

_____

_____

_____

_____

# NINE OF CUPS

**Keywords:** The granting of wishes, sensuality

**Meanings:** Great satisfaction. Contentment. Some consider this card the "wish" card—meaning a wish will be granted if this card appears in a spread. Earthly delights.

**Reversed or weakly aspected:** Delay in the granting of your wishes. Complacency. Taking a relationship for granted. Overindulgence. Inability to receive pleasure.

✧ ✧ ✧

FINALLY SATISFACTION! A rainbow leads the woman to a banquet table set with nine cups filled with delicious, rare wines. Surrounded by soft green grass and delicate pink flowers—pink being the sacred color of Venus—this table is covered with a rich blue cloth embroidered with golden moons; these decorations symbolizing the emotional riches offered by the Divine Feminine. Well worth waiting for, this sumptuous feast will nourish many bodies and souls. As the woman rests in this garden of earthly delights, she raises her cup in thanks.

The Nine of Cups offers the promise of bounty—at last all our hopes are fulfilled, our dreams realized. But the satisfaction depicted here can only be reached by journeying through the complicated emotional landscape explored in the earlier cards of this suit. As well, this card offers an omen that a wish will be granted in the near future. It's as if the world is giving us a reward for sheer persistence.

*If I could choose anything, for what would I wish?* _____

_____

_____

_____

*Some ways the world has shown me bounty:* _____

_____

_____

_____

_____

_____

*This card reminds me of the following:* _____

_____

_____

_____

_____

_____

_____

_____

*Other thoughts I have about this card:* _____

_____

_____

_____

_____

_____

_____

_____

_____

_____

_____

# TEN OF CUPS

**Keywords:** Joyful closure, endings, abundance, happiness

**Meanings:** Joyful completion. Happiness and joy. Happy family life. Abundance. Great emotional satisfaction. Endurance in love relationships. Fertility. Expansion.

**Reversed or weakly aspected**: An inability to allow joy to be experienced. Dissatisfaction though uncertain why—everything looks perfect on the surface.

✈ ✈ ✈

AS THE WOMAN GAZES from her celebratory feast, she sees the rainbow crowning a serene sky. Ten cups form a golden arc over it and are reflected in a calm ocean—the same ocean from which the goddess Venus was born, bringing love and harmony to all who would know these joys. The moon, symbolizing the robust pleasures of the Divine Feminine, is full and promises satisfaction, abundance, and love. As the woman gazes upon this beauteous scene, she decides that this is the best life can offer.

The Ten of Cups signifies a joyful end to the journey of emotions explored in the suit of cups. Here, we experience the abundance that happy relationships can offer: we please and we are pleased. This abundance can take various forms: the successful completion of creative projects, a happy marriage, even the start of our own family with children. It's as if our lives are so full of bounty that we want to share our good fortune with the world.

*When have I felt most blessed in my life?* _____

_____

_____

_____

_____

*What circumstances led to this happiness?* _____

_____

_____

_____

_____

_____

*This card reminds me of the following:* _____

_____

_____

_____

_____

_____

*Other thoughts I have about this card:* _____

_____

_____

_____

_____

_____

_____

_____

_____

_____

# PRINCE OF CUPS

**Keywords:** Gentleness, intuition, an invitation

**Meanings:** An invitation or offer. Gentleness. Children whose open hearts allow one to experience innocence anew. Intuition. Prophetic or inspiring dreams.

**Reversed or weakly aspected:** Disillusionment with an offer that promised more substance. Fickleness or immaturity of affection. Inconsistent or unreliable messages. Ambivalence.

৶ ৶ ৶

SURROUNDED BY A CALM OCEAN, the Prince of Cups, a gentle boy about to blossom into young adulthood, proffers a cup. It is decorated with the sacred symbols of Venus and the Divine Feminine, for whom he is a representative. The water within this cup is a magical potion—it can invite love, renewed passion, creative ventures and other wondrous riches that offer emotional sustenance. The darkened night sky and calm waters surrounding the Prince of Cups suggests a quiet acceptance of his offer.

The Prince of Cups can also symbolize the gentle voice of intuition that we all possess. To quiet ourselves and listen to this voice is to open ourselves up to the deep wisdom contained within ourselves—all we need to do is accept this invitation.

*How have I used intuition in my life?* _____

_____

_____

_____

_____

_____

*Some ways I can strengthen my intuition:* _____

_____

_____

_____

_____

_____

*This card reminds me of the following:* _____

_____

_____

_____

_____

_____

_____

_____

*Other thoughts I have about this card:* _____

_____

_____

_____

_____

_____

_____

_____

_____

_____

_____

# PRINCESS OF CUPS

*Keywords:* Inspiration, grace, pleasure

*Meanings:* Artistic inspiration and receptivity. Movement in these areas of life. Grace and talent. A young woman who symbolizes the gifts of Venus—love, beauty, and emotional richness—and inspires others to appreciation.

*Reversed or weakly aspected:* The need to be more receptive to beauty, love, and harmony. Over-indulgence in fantasies.

❧ ❧ ❧

THE PRINCESS OF CUPS, an adolescent girl as beautiful as Venus, is crowned with gold and a brilliant waxing moon. The sheer force of her allure attracts artistry, inspiration, and new opportunities. Anticipating love, pleasure and the ripeness of womanhood, she drinks fully of the cup's refreshing contents. As she drinks, she closes her eyes to take in the fullness of her spirit—all she offers to those who experience her serene graceful presence.

The appearance of the Princess of Cups suggests the seductive qualities of inspiration, the ability to influence others with artistic gifts. All we need to do is to appreciate these gifts enough to develop them. If we are serious about ourselves, others will take us seriously in return—acknowledgement is only a matter of time.

*What artistic gifts would I like to develop?* _____

_____

_____

_____

_____

_____

*Some ways I can develop my talents:*_____

_____

_____

_____

_____

_____

*This card reminds me of the following:* _____

_____

_____

_____

_____

_____

_____

*Other thoughts I have about this card:*_____

_____

_____

_____

_____

_____

_____

_____

_____

_____

# KING OF CUPS

*Keywords:* Practical artistry, mastery, creative control

*Meanings:* Ability to live up to ideals and dreams. Combining artistic integrity with the needs of the marketplace. Emotional maturity and integrity. Someone who symbolizes these forces.

*Reversed or weakly aspected:* Desire to have more control over one's artistic aspirations. Need to stop dreaming up schemes and get to work. Inconsistency.

✤ ✤ ✤

THE KING OF CUPS, a thoughtful older man who is quiet and serene in nature, sits upon his throne. He is surrounded by water, symbolizing his authority over the world of emotions and intuition. As he meditates upon the single cup held within his hand, he is entranced by the potential promised to him by the Divine Feminine. Masterful and artistic, the King of Cups is able to express himself in his relationships and work. He is a consort worthy of any follower of the goddess Venus.

How would it feel to own your talents, to be considered an authority? This card is reminder of how good it feels to be honored—and paid accordingly—for our talents. To reach this point takes a certain amount of self-esteem as well as an awareness of our place within the marketplace. The King of Cups is a worthy example of the success available to those who have reached this happy place.

*What talents do I possess?* _____

_____

_____

_____

_____

*How do they relate to the way I make money?* _____

_____

_____

_____

_____

_____

*This card reminds me of the following:* _____

_____

_____

_____

_____

_____

*Other thoughts I have about this card:* _____

_____

_____

_____

_____

_____

_____

_____

_____

_____

# QUEEN OF CUPS

*Keywords:* Soulfulness, emotion, inspiration

*Meanings:* Mastery of all that Venus—and the suit of cups—represents: art, beauty, intimacy, love. The ability to express love, to nurture others. An older woman who inspires others to live harmoniously.

*Reversed or weakly aspected:* Overwhelmed by emotions that need sorting. Need to take control of these feelings. Not mining the treasures of the soul. Disharmonious relationships with women—or with the self.

❧ ❧ ❧

THE FULL MOON is a halo around the heavy golden crown of the majestic Queen of Cups. Holding all wisdom and intuition within herself, she is more soul than body. As she holds a single cup, a profusion of pearls dot her gown and headdress; these jewels from the sea symbolize the emotional fertile forces of the Divine Feminine. Like the sea herself, the Queen of Cups' regal mysterious presence inspires people to look within. She knows the treasures found there will nourish the heart.

The Queen of Cups represents complete mastery over the world of emotions presented in the suit of cups. Within ourselves is the ability to feel profound joy and appreciate intense beauty. The presence of this card suggests a new awareness of this state of grace. Whether found inside ourselves or recognized in another person, we are truly blessed.

*Description of a time when I felt profound joy:* _____

_____

_____

_____

_____

*Description of a time when I felt inspiration:* ⸻

_____

_____

_____

_____

_____

_____

*This card reminds me of the following:* ⸻

_____

_____

_____

_____

_____

_____

_____

_____

*Other thoughts I have about this card:* ⸻

_____

_____

_____

_____

_____

_____

_____

_____

_____

_____

ACE

STAVES

TWO

STAVES

THREE

STAVES

FOUR

STAVES

QUEEN

STAVES

FIVE

STAVES

KING

STAVES

SIX

STAVES

## Part Three:
# THE MINOR ARCANA

## The Suit of Staves

PRINCESS

STAVES

SEVEN

STAVES

PRINCE

STAVES

TEN

STAVES

NINE

STAVES

EIGHT

STAVES

*Element: Fire, the sun*
*Corresponds to Power, Major Arcana card number 4*

The suit of staves is related to Freyja, the Norse goddess of creativity, fertility and beauty. In the progression of the minor arcana's suits, staves are like new tree saplings breaking through the earth—fertile earth that has been anointed with water from the preceding suit of cups.

Staves are the active aspect of the Divine Feminine, differing from the receptive forces expressed in the suit of cups. Like conduits of the sun's procreative force, they channel intense energy to areas of our lives where they can encourage growth. Staves bring exciting movement to a tarot reading—much like the movement displayed by Freyja as she flies through the sky in her chariot drawn by magical grey cats or with her magical falcon skin cloak.

The appearance of staves in a tarot reading offers the electrical power of creativity, the promise of expansion. After incubating our most precious ideas and projects within ourselves, now is the time to share them with the world.

### THE MYTH OF FREYJA ✧ ✧ ✧

In Norse mythology, gods and goddesses are divided into two groups, the Vanir and the Aesir. The peaceful Vanir grew food from the earth and were worshiped during the agricultural Bronze Age. Later, when the first tools and weapons were developed with forge and fire, the combative Aesir came into existence. The Aesir brought war and discord into the bucolic world of the Vanir. Desiring peace at any price, the Vanir offered the Aesir their most precious possession: Freyja, daughter of Njord, the god of fair winds.

In this way, Freyja became a mediator between peace and violence. A goddess of creativity, sexuality, and beauty, she also became known as the goddess who presided over the living and the dead. It was Freyja who was responsible for the souls of half of the warriors felled in battle. Upon their death, these men were brought to her grand hall in Asgard, where they were feted with epic poems of brave deeds and accorded honor. There, these men existed through eternity surrounded by the luxurious pleasures sacred to this powerful goddess.

Also sacred to Freyja were the pragmatic arts of goldsmithing and jewelry making — crafts which take the raw materials of the earth and turn them into beautiful treasures. No doubt in acknowledgment of this, Freyja was said never to be seen without her favorite necklace, Brisingamen. Even today, this goddess's influence continues—the Norse still refer to the Milky Way as "Freyja's necklace."

## An Overview of the Suit of Staves, the Path of Freyja ⊹ ⊹ ⊹

| MINOR ARCANA CARD | KEY WORDS |
|---|---|
| Ace of Staves | *inspiration, growth, action* |
| Two of Staves | *new ventures, partnership, ideas* |
| Three of Staves | *successful enterprises, planning* |
| Four of Staves | *stability, creating a home, structure* |
| Five of Staves | *conflict, competition, dissension* |
| Six of Staves | *victory, acknowledgement, honor* |
| Seven of Staves | *defense, combat, struggle* |
| Eight of Staves | *sudden communications, movement* |
| Nine of Staves | *responsibility, separation, exhaustion* |
| Ten of Staves | *cumulation, success, creativity* |
| Prince of Staves | *new ideas, communications* |
| Princess of Staves | *passion, integrity, action, inspiration* |
| King of Staves | *enthusiasm, mastery, support* |
| Queen of Staves | *power, cleverness, beauty, confidence* |

# ACE OF STAVES

**Keywords:** Inspiration, growth, action

**Meaning:** The active principle of the Divine Feminine. Great energy that flows unbounded. Beginning of a focused, creative period. Inspiration that inspires action. New opportunities. The active or yang, aspect of life. Growth.

**Reversed or weakly aspected:** Difficulties with new ventures. Being "burned" out by too much energy, too much expenditure, too many thoughts. The need to focus.

⌖ ⌖ ⌖

UPON A VERDANT HILL dotted with tiny red flowers, a single sapling grows. It yearns toward the sky, just like Freyja in her magical chariot drawn by grey cats. New leaves twist from its knotty stubborn surface, revealing the vigorous growth surging within its depths. Behind this single stave, the fiery sun—symbolizing the Divine Feminine's dynamic life force which inspires us to grow and prosper—rises upon a distant mountain range. It is the start of a new day with new possibilities for action, as well as new opportunities for growth.

The Ace of Staves promises the start of a more active phase of our lives, one in which much activity will be focused toward a worthy goal. Like a mighty tree attracting lightning from the heavens, it's as if we are channeling electricity from above. All we need to do is let this energy work through us.

*Where would I like to have more action in my life?* _____

_____

_____

_____

_____

*Some creative projects I'd like to jumpstart:* _____

_____

_____

_____

_____

_____

*This card reminds me of the following:* _____

_____

_____

_____

_____

_____

_____

_____

*Other thoughts I have about this card:* _____

_____

_____

_____

_____

_____

_____

_____

_____

_____

_____

# TWO OF STAVES

**Keywords:** New ventures, partnership, ideas

**Meanings:** Beginnings of a new venture, possibly business-oriented in nature. A dynamic partnership. New ideas that transform lives and energize people. Transforming inspiration into action.

**Reversed or weakly aspected:** A good start to a venture that eventually loses momentum. Disappointment in projects. Frustration or impatience.

✧ ✧ ✧

INSPIRED BY NEW IDEAS, the woman watches the sun rise and plans how to bring her vision into the world. Two staves stand on each side of her. The stave she holds in her left hand symbolizes her receptivity to new ideas; the other stave represents her aspirations in the world beyond her. She is dressed in a red gown—the color of vigor and beginnings—as she surveys the mountain range within sight from her ornately walled terrace. She has the confidence and talent of Freyja, the goddess of creativity; this combination ensures she will meet success.

The Two of Staves signifies the concrete beginning of a new venture, a dynamic partnership that will fulfill us. It also offers us the challenge of taking our ideas and implementing them. To do this, we often need the assistance of others. This card announces the possibility of finding a like minded partner who will help us bring our plans into the world where they can take on a life of their own.

*With what new ventures do I need help?*_____

_____

_____

_____

*Parts of my venture I can delegate:* _____

_____

_____

_____

_____

_____

*This card remind me of the following:* _____

_____

_____

_____

_____

_____

_____

_____

*Other thoughts I have about this card:* _____

_____

_____

_____

_____

_____

_____

_____

_____

_____

# THREE OF STAVES

**Keywords:** Successful enterprises, planning

**Meanings:** An enterprise about to cumulate in success. The ability to transform goals into realistic action. Business success after a successful launching. Activity with clear intent.

**Reversed or weakly aspected:** Ambitious plans which may not be grounded in reality. A frustrating delay in receiving success.

✧ ✧ ✧

THE WOMAN TRAVELS AND FINALLY ARRIVES at a calm sea framed by three staves. Reflected within the sea's depths are the first fiery rays of the sun, symbolizing the emotional resolve that enabled her to take action. Her intentions are as pure as the white gown she wears; the red belt around her waist represents energy that transforms intention into creation. Grasping one of the three staves, the woman contemplates her plans; she is waiting for her ships to come in, knowing they will bring the success and bountiful treasures so loved by the goddess Freyja.

Often appearing before the successful cumulation of an new venture, the presence of the Three of Staves in a tarot reading offers the promise that our hard work and determination will pay off. We have traveled a long road to reach this happy place. Now all we need to do is wait.

*Where am I waiting for success in my life?* _____

_____

_____

_____

_____

*What have I done to encourage it?* _____

_____

_____

_____

_____

_____

*This card reminds me of the following:* _____

_____

_____

_____

_____

_____

_____

_____

_____

*Other thoughts I have about this card:* _____

_____

_____

_____

_____

_____

_____

_____

_____

_____

# FOUR OF STAVES

*Keywords:* Stability, creating a home, structure

*Meanings:* Stability of ventures. A new home. Accomplishing goals and enjoying them. First success of a new venture. Satisfaction. Putting down roots. Possibly a marriage or domestic partnership. Helpful structure.

*Reversed or weakly aspected:* The desire to put down roots, but elusiveness in doing so. Frustrations or disappointments at home. Wanting stability.

✤ ✤ ✤

THE WOMAN FINDS FOUR STAVES securely planted upon a grassy hill. These staves are joined together at their tops with bounteous garlands dotted with red roses; they suggest the stable foundation of a happy home. Within the four staves' perimeters, the woman is joined by her beloved. To them, these four staves represent the first flowering of their vision. Together they dance to celebration and success. In the distance Asgard, the mythic castle that serves as home to Freyja, can be seen. It symbolizes the ideal home we all aspire to create for ourselves in an ideal world.

The Four of Staves is an invitation to create this home in our lives. Imagine the home is a microcosm of the universe surrounding us: if our home is stable and harmonious, we will feel all is well with our world. Often we are only able to create this home after we attain certain life goals we've set for ourselves. In this case, the home becomes a reflection of our successful career and personal life.

*What would my ideal home be like?* _____

_____

_____

_____

*How is my current home like this ideal home?* _____

_____

_____

_____

_____

_____

_____

*This card reminds me of the following:* _____

_____

_____

_____

_____

_____

_____

_____

_____

*Other thoughts I have about this card:* _____

_____

_____

_____

_____

_____

_____

_____

_____

_____

_____

# FIVE OF STAVES

**Keywords:** Conflict, competition, dissension

**Meanings:** Inability to focus or move. Dissension, which may be within the psyche or personified in the people around you. Conflict for the sake of conflict. Ego-oriented competition. Losing sight of what's important because of petty disagreements.

**Reversed or weakly aspected:** Moving beyond petty concerns and worries to understand what's important. Unifying forces. Overcoming obstacles.

⊹ ⊹ ⊹

IN A DREAM, the woman sees five conflicting aspects of herself, each one a warrior armed with a stave. They use these five staves to fight amongst themselves in a broiling hot desert landscape. The intense rays of the sun heats everyone's tempers, making it all the more difficult to distinguish what the fight is really about—after all, aren't they on the same team? When the woman finally wakes from this dream, she feels disturbed. She is reminded of her limitations, her inability to move ahead. She wonders what to do but is too proud to ask for help.

The Five of Staves represents life situations where we feel blocked. To overcome this blockage, we are willing to forget all that is important to us, and to engage in meaningless conflict. We seek to blame whatever it is that we are fighting—failing to see that the situation surrounding us is only a reflection of our inner frustrations.

*Where do I feel conflict in my life?* _____

_____

_____

_____

_____

*How do I feel blocked in my life?* _____

_____

_____

_____

_____

_____

*This card reminds me of the following:* _____

_____

_____

_____

_____

_____

_____

_____

_____

*Other thoughts I have about this card:* _____

_____

_____

_____

_____

_____

_____

_____

_____

_____

_____

# SIX OF STAVES

**Keywords:** Victory, acknowledgement, honor

**Meanings:** Victory! Enjoying success after much hard work and struggle. Acknowledgement and honor from those around you. The fruits of courage and integrity. Integration and harmony.

**Reversed or weakly aspected:** Victory is elusive. You've done the work, you deserve the honors, but they haven't come—perhaps because of a lack of awareness in those around you.

✧ ✧ ✧

FINALLY, A RESOLUTION IS REACHED. In triumph, the woman rides a docile horse adorned in red and white; these dressings are embroidered with gold, the precious metal most sacred to the goddess Freyja. As the woman shares her joyful news with the world, she is surrounded by six staves, one which bears the laurels of victory. Another laurel is placed upon her brow, anointing her as the winner. The staves about her are raised in tribute of her courage and stamina in the face of adversity.

The appearance of the Six of Staves in a tarot reading offers the promise of victory after the inner struggle explored in the previous card of this suit. Here, honor and acknowledgement are ours—they are sweet and well deserved.

*Where would I like to experience victory?* _____

_____

_____

_____

_____

_____

*Some times I've felt victorious:*

_____

_____

_____

_____

_____

*This card reminds me of the following:*

_____

_____

_____

_____

_____

_____

_____

_____

*Other thoughts I have about this card:*

_____

_____

_____

_____

_____

_____

_____

_____

_____

_____

# SEVEN OF STAVES

**Keywords:** Defense, struggle, combat

**Meanings:** Instability and struggle. While you may have the ultimate advantage in this situation, there is still conflict. Success is possible, but only after dealing with difficult people who oppose your plans. Remember, they have their own agendas to consider.

**Reversed or weakly aspected:** Indecisiveness in the face of opposition. Feeling overwhelmed. Creating problems for oneself in order to distract from what is really going on.

✦ ✦ ✦

ATTACKED BY SIX STAVES, the woman is trapped at the edge of a dangerous cliff. Against her will she is forced to defend herself. She does so using a seventh stave. Despite the promise of the clear blue sky that curves over the landscape beneath her, the hot sun scorches the woman's shoulders. Unable to get out of the heat, she feels attacked from all sides. While she has a position of advantage in this struggle, she needs to draw upon the warrior energy of the goddess Freyja to ultimately win this battle.

Instability and struggle are hallmarks of the Seven of Staves. By dealing with difficult people who have their own agendas, we are forced to reconsider our own. This can either foster us with additional confidence or undermine us with insecurities. However the appearance of this card suggests that victory is eventually possible—but only after much unpleasantness.

*Where do I feel I need to defend myself?* _____

_____

_____

_____

_____

*What people create conflict in my life?* _____

_____
_____
_____
_____
_____

*This card reminds me of the following:* _____

_____
_____
_____
_____
_____
_____
_____
_____
_____
_____

*Other thoughts I have about this card:* _____

_____
_____
_____
_____
_____
_____
_____
_____
_____
_____
_____
_____

# EIGHT OF STAVES

*Keywords:* Sudden movement, communications

*Meanings:* Important communications—unexpected telephone calls, surprise letters—which release uncertainties and end waiting. Energetic movement. Quickness and suddenness. Unknown information finally released that makes sense.

*Reversed or weakly aspected:* Waiting too long for communication. Perhaps it is time to take the initiative to create waves. Stop waiting for others to make the first move.

✧ ✧ ✧

LOOKING OUT FROM THE EDGE OF THE CLIFF, the woman sees eight staves positioned like sudden lightning from the heavens. These staves dash like brilliant electricity, bringing important news and communications. Their message is one of excitement; of help and rescue; of fortuitous timing and information that brim with long awaited truths. These staves crack across a dramatic sky filled with storm clouds—clouds that protect the woman from the intense sun.

The Eight of Staves offers welcome release from a frustrating lack of communication. This flurry of new information makes us feel as though the world is moving about us again—we are full of hope and anticipation at what may happen next. Finally we learn what we need to know so we can move forward with confidence.

*What information do I lack at this time?* _____

_____

_____

_____

_____

_____

*Some ways I can take action:* _____

_____

_____

_____

_____

_____

*This card reminds me of the following:* _____

_____

_____

_____

_____

_____

_____

*Other thoughts I have about this card:* _____

_____

_____

_____

_____

_____

_____

_____

_____

_____

# NINE OF STAVES

**Keywords:** Responsibility, separation, exhaustion

**Meanings:** A pause in work to rest, to reconsider plans. Completion is so close, yet so far away! Need for protection or separation from others who may not be fully supportive in order to finish a project. Exhaustion or overresponsibility.

**Reversed or weakly aspected:** Feeling overwhelmed by work. Need for a break. Not fully acknowledging the work needed to finish a project. Denial of responsibilities.

✧ ✧ ✧

FINALLY THE WOMAN UNDERSTANDS—but she also understands how much work she needs to do to complete the project she wants to share with the world. Temporarily protected by a wall of staves, the woman rests for a moment to catch her breath. As she does so, she struggles with her overwhelming responsibilities. There is so much to do before total success can be reached. But first the woman's thoughts and plans must be regrouped before she can continue.

The appearance of the Nine of Staves presents us with a portrait of total exhaustion. The lesson ultimately offered by this card is one of patience—though success is close at hand, we need to rest first. This delay may be frustrating but ultimately we will be able to think more clearly, work more effectively. Part of our exhaustion may also come from dealing with people who are not as supportive of us as we'd like them to be. We cannot change them, but we can give ourselves the space we need to regain our strength.

*Where do I feel overwhelmed in my work?*_____

_____

_____

_____

*How do I pace myself while working?* _____

_____

_____

_____

_____

_____

*This card reminds me of the following:* _____

_____

_____

_____

_____

_____

_____

_____

_____

*Other thoughts I have about this card:* _____

_____

_____

_____

_____

_____

_____

_____

_____

_____

_____

_____

# TEN OF STAVES

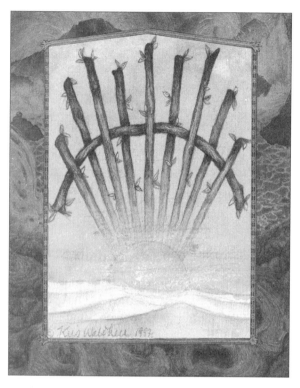

*Keywords:* Cumulation, success, creativity

*Meanings:* The cumulation of the creative venture begun with the one of staves. Success that becomes overwhelming with its responsibility. The final vision is within reach, but work can be oppressive.

*Reversed or weakly aspected:* Overwhelmed and burdened by responsibilities. No time to enjoy success—there's too much work to do!

✢ ✢ ✢

FROM HER PLACE OF PROTECTION the woman sees a glorious sunset. She is optimistic it foretells her victory. Within this sunset radiates ten staves, each symbolizing the creative promise of Freyja. The green leaves upon each stave shows they are natural extensions of the sun's warm, life-giving force—this force symbolizing the dynamic, growth-inducing aspect of the Divine Feminine. While it is affirming to see the bounty promised by this scene, there is so much energy it's easy to feel burned.

The Ten of Staves offers the completion of the journey begun with the Ace of Staves—here creative ventures have successfully expanded into the world, success has been gained. Our final vision is within reach, but work is still needed. However sometimes this card shows us that the work is within us: as wonderful as success can be, it can encourage new tensions and self-doubts.

*Where would I like to see success in my life?* _____

_____

_____

_____

_____

*How would I handle success?* _____

_____
_____
_____
_____
_____

*This card reminds me of the following:* _____

_____
_____
_____
_____
_____
_____

*Other thoughts I have about this card:* _____

_____
_____
_____
_____
_____
_____
_____
_____
_____

# PRINCE OF STAVES

*Keywords:* New ideas, inspiration, communications

*Meanings:* Important communications. Need to listen to inspiration, new ideas. However these should be weighed according to practicality. An inexperienced young person who may be very passionate but not very pragmatic because of inexperience.

*Reversed or weakly aspected:* Too much energy and not enough focus. Ideas and messages that fizzle out after initial enthusiasm. Inconsistency. Overenthusiasm for the sake of emotional display.

✤ ✤ ✤

THE PRINCE OF STAVES is the bearer of important messages—messages that will either jolt us into action or bring awareness of what can be accomplished using the wisdom of Freyja. As he walks in a rocky landscape, he holds a leafy staff to support himself. A passionate wind, symbolic of the enthusiastic ideas he loves to share with the world, blows his brilliant red cloak. Unfortunately he is too young to be able to carry out his ideas, but he is able to inspire others with them.

The Prince of Staves is a inciter to action. Wherever he appears in a tarot reading, expect to feel the support of others. They may not be able to help you, but their positive enthusiasm will get you moving. Sometimes this is just what we need—a bright, brilliant, inspiring force to remind us of what we can accomplish once we put our minds to it.

*What people or situations inspire me to action?* _____

_____

_____

_____

_____

*With what ideas have they inspired me?* _____

_____

_____

_____

_____

_____

_____

*This card reminds me of the following:* _____

_____

_____

_____

_____

_____

_____

*Other thoughts I have about this card:*_____

_____

_____

_____

_____

_____

_____

_____

_____

_____

# PRINCESS OF STAVES

**Keywords:** Passion, integrity, action, inspiration

**Meanings:** The ability to create beauty that has use in the world. Energy, integrity and creativity. Initiative. New ideas or ventures that must be acted upon immediately. A young woman who inspires others to live this mission.

**Reversed or weakly aspected:** Scattered energy. Inability to focus on matters at hand. Need to develop skills to bring dreams into reality. Too much energy or not enough energy.

✧ ✧ ✧

THE PRINCESS OF STAVES, a fiery-haired young woman wearing a circle of gold upon her brow, vows to be as stalwart as the rocks surrounding her. Her passionate example is an inspiration to live with intent and without compromise. Yearning to experience all of life's fullness, embracing all its possibilities, she glorifies Freyja's favored values of beauty, creativity and hard work. She carries within herself a strength of character that will win followers as she presents her creative vision to the world.

The Princess of Staves' ability to move forward with her work exemplifies the expansive quality of confidence at its best. Whenever this card appears, know that any work shared with the world at this time will be enthusiastically received—the integrity inherently held within it will easily win others' support. All self-doubts are to be banished as you move forward.

*Where would I like to feel more confident?*_____

_____

_____

_____

_____

*Some projects on which I would like to move forward:* ___

_____

_____

_____

_____

_____

_____

*This card reminds me of the following:* _____

_____

_____

_____

_____

_____

_____

_____

*Other thoughts I have about this card:* _____

_____

_____

_____

_____

_____

_____

_____

_____

_____

_____

# KING OF STAVES

**Keywords:** Enthusiasm, mastery, support

**Meanings:** Dynamic, stable enthusiasm. Mastery over business ventures. The ability to bring ideas to fruition. Someone who symbolizes these strengths. Creative inspiration and help.

**Reversed or weakly aspected:** Wanting to harness these forces, but not quite strong enough to do so. Someone who seems supportive, but when push comes to shove has already lost interest.

✢ ✢ ✢

DRESSED IN HEAVY ROBES decorated with gold embroidery depicting the sun, the King of Staves represents the epitome of the sun's power. As he sits upon his throne, his regal, expansive and energizing personality creates opportunities where none existed before. The authority so easily exercised by the King of Staves enables him to make certain these opportunities will reach fruition.

Perhaps more importantly, the King of Staves has the happy talent of inspiring growth in others. For those who welcome his advice, his supportive friendship offers encouragement; his passionate enthusiasm strengthens wavering confidence. Through the warmth of his presence, life becomes an expansive experience.

*Where do I need more encouragement?*_____

_____

_____

_____

_____

_____

*What authority figures do I feel support me?* _____

_____

_____

_____

_____

_____

*This card reminds me of the following:* _____

_____

_____

_____

_____

_____

_____

_____

_____

*Other thoughts I have about this card:* _____

_____

_____

_____

_____

_____

_____

_____

_____

_____

_____

_____

# QUEEN OF STAVES

*Keywords:* Power, beauty, confidence, cleverness

*Meanings:* Intelligence applied to creating material goods, business expansion. Cleverness. A woman who embodies these ideas and inspires action from others. Wit and wisdom. Enthusiasm and action. Support.

*Reversed or weakly aspected:* Waiting too long to use your forces. Not showing the world your talents. Undermining your authority. Lack of self worth or low self esteem.

✤ ✤ ✤

POWER AND ENERGY are held in reserve by the beautiful, bejeweled Queen of Staves. Similar to her consort the King of Staves, she is dressed in robes embroidered with gold suns. While she might seem passive as she holds court upon her rocky throne, only a moment's notice is needed to rouse her to action. Like Freyja, the Queen of Staves' majestic qualities can inspire the creation of beauty through practical applications; she also possesses enough cleverness to implement these ideas herself.

The welcome appearance of the Queen of Staves in a tarot reading reassures that we have the talent and initiative necessary to transform our fondest schemes into reality. But perhaps more importantly, we now have the strength and confidence to bring them into the world. This unstoppable combination of creative inspiration and pragmatic action will ensure our success.

*What pet project would I like to make real?* _____

_____

_____

_____

_____

*What talents can I use to ensure its success?* _____

_____

_____

_____

_____

_____

*This card reminds me of the following:* _____

_____

_____

_____

_____

_____

_____

_____

*Other thoughts I have about this card:* _____

_____

_____

_____

_____

_____

_____

_____

_____

_____

_____

_____

ACE

SWORDS

TWO

SWORDS

THREE

SWORDS

FOUR

SWORDS

QUEEN

SWORDS

KING

SWORDS

PRINCESS

SWORDS

PRINCE

SWORDS

TEN

SWORDS

NINE

SWORDS

*Chapter Four:*

# THE MINOR ARCANA

## The Suit of Swords

FIVE

SWORDS

SIX

SWORDS

SEVEN

SWORDS

EIGHT

SWORDS

## Element: Air, salt
## Corresponds to Magic, Major Arcana card number 1

The suit of swords is associated with Isis, the Egyptian fertility goddess. Swords symbolize the incisive forces of the intellect—they cut through and focus the energy grown in the preceding suit of staves. Think of swords as the shears that prune weak branches from the sapling tree so that it can strengthen and bear fruit; this pruning may seem severe but ultimately it is a necessary life-giving action.

When swords appear in a tarot reading, they serve to remind us of the Divine Feminine's ability to transform painful situations into areas of personal growth. The myth of Isis and her consort Osiris illustrates this affirming principle beautifully. Like Isis, we can choose how to use our swords: we can turn them against ourselves when we are in pain. Or we can transform the situation through knowledge and understanding, the better to gain mastery over our lives.

### THE MYTH OF ISIS ✧ ✧ ✧

The story of Isis shows us the transformative powers of love, grief, death and rebirth. For over three thousand years—from before 3000 B.C. to the second century A.D.—Isis was worshiped in Egypt as the Great Mother Goddess of the Universe. Isis looked after the affairs of the day while her sister, Nephthys, took care of the night. She also had two brothers, Osiris and Set. Osiris was responsible for the fertile soil and Set ruled the barren desert. When they were old enough, the sun god Ra married Isis to Osiris and Set to Nephthys. Isis and Osiris were blissful in their love and were adored by many; no moon could compare to the bliss of their passion, no sun to the brightness of their honor. Set saw this and jealousy ate at his soul, giving him no rest. So he entrapped his brother in a coffin, and heaved him into the swirling waters of the Nile.

Grief-stricken, Isis transformed herself into a dark bird and flew everywhere searching for her beloved Osiris. Finally, she found the coffin embedded in a tree. Isis hid the coffin from Set. But Set learned all, and he mercilessly cut Osiris' body into fourteen pieces and scattered them in all four directions.

Isis was not deterred. She traveled up and down the Nile in a papyrus boat, searching for the pieces of her lost husband and brother. When she had found them all, she placed them next to each other and, with the power of her love, briefly brought her husband back to life. That last act of love resulted in Isis conceiving a child, Horus, the falcon-headed god. Together Isis and Horus were able to bring Set to justice for the murder of Osiris.

An Overview of the Suit of Swords, the Path of Isis ☙ ☙ ☙

| MINOR ARCANA CARD | KEY WORDS |
| --- | --- |
| Ace of Swords | *wisdom, understanding, intelligence* |
| Two of Swords | *peace, truce, impasse, uneasiness* |
| Three of Swords | *heartbreak, grief, oversensitivity* |
| Four of Swords | *healing, introspection, meditation* |
| Five of Swords | *discomfort, struggle, distrust* |
| Six of Swords | *transitions, travel, movement* |
| Seven of Swords | *defense, caution, vulnerability* |
| Eight of Swords | *depression, entrapment, self-victimization* |
| Nine of Swords | *anxiety, unresolved issues, insomnia* |
| Ten of Swords | *understanding, endings, wisdom* |
| Prince of Swords | *messages, influence, articulation* |
| Princess of Swords | *decisiveness, clarity, defense* |
| King of Swords | *authority, responsibility, detachment* |
| Queen of Swords | *brilliance, honesty, clarity* |

# ACE OF SWORDS

**Keywords:** Wisdom, intelligence, understanding

**Meanings:** The incisive powers of the Divine Feminine. Pure understanding and wisdom. The ability to wield your "sword" wisely. Clarity and good judgment. Knowing the difference between right and wrong. Intelligence. Truth. Beginning of a cycle of intellectual growth.

**Reversed or weakly aspected:** Need for thought. Are you using your swords against yourself or as a tool for growth? Self-recrimination and rejection of personal power to blame others. Confusion.

✤ ✤ ✤

A GREY SKY reveals a desolate desert set with pyramids, the final resting place of the pharaohs of ancient Egypt. Within a mound of sand stands a single sword. Its defiant presence is a challenge to those who would wield it to gain the riches stored within the pharaohs' tombs. The sword's ornate gold handle is decorated with the horned symbol of Isis, the Egyptian goddess of wisdom and fertility; it is also shaped like the lotus, the flower of spiritual enlightenment. But it is the sword's sharp blade that bears the symbol of the Divine Feminine, symbolizing her incisive powers of intellect.

The Ace of Swords offers us a valuable tool—the wisdom of pure understanding. The appearance of this card symbolizes the beginning of a new phase of life in which much intellectual growth will be made. Sometimes this learning may come easily; other times this education may be gained through painful life experience—but its value is priceless.

*How do I feel about education?* _____

_____

_____

_____

_____

*How do I feel about wisdom?*_____

_____

_____

_____

_____

_____

*This card reminds me of the following:* _____

_____

_____

_____

_____

_____

_____

*Other thoughts I have about this card:*_____

_____

_____

_____

_____

_____

_____

_____

_____

_____

# TWO OF SWORDS

**Keywords:** Peace, truce, impasse, uneasiness

**Meanings:** Peaceful or temporary truce. Understanding a difficult situation. Balance attained, but eventually issues will have to be confronted. Inability to change; the ability to accept. Emotional control.

**Reversed or weakly aspected:** Discomfort with a decision. Overreliance on intellect, leaving emotions unconsidered. Uncomfortable relationships.

⭗ ⭗ ⭗

AN IMPASSE IS MET. To better look within, the woman has blindfolded herself; this way she will not be confused by too much information or others' opinions. The Nile River flows behind her, symbolizing the conflicting emotions she has turned her back upon for now. The perfection of the woman's inner balance is symbolized by the lotus blossoms surrounding her and by the two swords she has balanced within her arms. If she needs these swords, they are ready to be used—but for now all is peaceful.

The Two of Swords is a reminder to us of the sometimes transitory quality of peace. While a truce has been made, circumstances are not as ideal as we would like. Luckily we have the wisdom necessary to recognize that this is the best we can do. Issues will eventually have to be confronted anew, but hopefully by then we will have more information to help us navigate our way through these confusing waters.

*Where am I at peace with conflict in my life?* _____

_____

_____

_____

_____

*How did I attain this peace?* _____

_____

_____

_____

_____

_____

_____

*This card reminds me of the following:* _____

_____

_____

_____

_____

_____

_____

_____

_____

*Other thoughts I have about this card:* _____

_____

_____

_____

_____

_____

_____

_____

_____

_____

_____

_____

# THREE OF SWORDS

*Keywords:* Heartbreak, grief, over-sensitivity

*Meanings:* A sharp pain to the heart—disappointment, end of a love relationship, separation. Sorrow that can enlighten or debilitate. Oversensitivity. Time for healing. The need to transform grief into understanding.

*Reversed or weakly aspected:* Overindulging in grief for the sake of drama. Identifying with the drama rather than the loss. Slow easing of sorrow.

✧ ✧ ✧

FLOATING IN AN INTENSE GREY SKY, a heart is pierced by three swords. This wounded heart also bears the eye of Isis superimposed upon it, representing the sorrow experienced by Isis upon the death of her beloved Osiris. The stormy sky surrounding it threatens rain which will bring needed release, like tears to a grief stricken soul. Despite the sadness of this scene, all is not lost. The symbol of the Divine Feminine is etched upon the heart, promising healing and compassion to those most in need of it.

The Three of Swords offers wisdom from the introspection often gained from loss. The pain represented by this card can be as sharp as a knife to the heart. But even in deepest sorrow we are offered an opportunity: we can transform our grief into under-standing. It takes great strength of character to embrace potential when there is so much loss. Luckily, this card shows us we are supported more than we know.

*What is the worst heartbreak I've ever felt?* _____

_____

_____

_____

_____

*Ways I grew from this difficult time:* _____

_____

_____

_____

_____

_____

*This card reminds me of the following:* _____

_____

_____

_____

_____

_____

_____

*Other thoughts I have about this card:* _____

_____

_____

_____

_____

_____

_____

_____

_____

# FOUR OF SWORDS

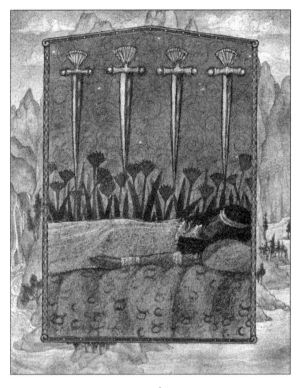

*Keywords:* Healing, introspection, meditation

*Meanings:* Introspection. Solitude. Need time to heal or rest. Detachment from the everyday world to regain balance. Recuperation from illness. Take a break from stressful situations.

*Reversed or weakly aspected:* Enforced isolation. Loneliness. More recovery time needed than what has been allowed. Needing more time alone.

✤ ✤ ✤

TO HEAL HERSELF, the woman rests upon a pallet hidden among rushes; the horned symbol of Isis is embroidered upon her royal purple bedclothes. As the woman recuperates, four swords are magically suspended above her amid a swirling starry sky. They protect her from the outside world, allowing her the space she needs to regain her strength. In time, the woman will again be as strong as Isis; she will be able to transform her problems through her powerful wisdom. But for now, she needs rest.

When life is stressful, the appearance of the Four of Swords in a reading is a strong reminder to give ourselves time alone. Often stress can create situations in which we can't see the forest for the trees, thus compounding any problems we might have. In worst case scenarios, it can also make us more susceptible to physical illness. The Four of Swords is a reminder that the best protection is sometimes retreat.

*What signs tell me I need to retreat?*_____

_____

_____

_____

_____

*Description of a time when I needed time alone:* _____

_____

_____

_____

_____

_____

_____

*This card reminds me of the following:* _____

_____

_____

_____

_____

_____

_____

_____

_____

*Other thoughts I have about this card:*_____

_____

_____

_____

_____

_____

_____

_____

_____

_____

_____

# FIVE OF SWORDS

*Keywords:* Discomfort, struggle, distrust

*Meanings:* An uncomfortable truce, but is the conflict really over? "Arming" oneself just in case of attack. Lack of trust. Possible defeat or feelings of defeat. The need for self-protection or caution. Discomfort or struggle with a situation.

*Reversed or weakly aspected:* Disingenuous surrender. Defeat because of indecisiveness. Paranoia. Dishonesty.

✤ ✤ ✤

COMPLETELY REJUVENATED FROM HER TIME ALONE, the woman moves on. She finally arrives at an arid landscape where she finds five heavy swords. Two of these abandoned swords have been laid down in a position of surrender. She doesn't fully trust this offering: as she scans the distance for enemies, she collects three of these swords, one which she places in her right hand in readiness. If necessary, she will be as fierce as Isis in her search for vengeance.

The Five of Swords offers an uncomfortable truce that may not warrant our trust. To accept this peace offering requires that we make ourselves vulnerable to attack, thus opening up a possible situation where our enemies may defeat us after all. The appearance of this card is a strong reminder to protect ourselves, just in case. Preparation can be the best defense.

*Where do I feel vulnerable in my life?* _____

_____

_____

_____

_____

*What makes this situation uncomfortable?* _____

_____

_____

_____

_____

_____

*This card reminds me of the following:* _____

_____

_____

_____

_____

_____

_____

_____

_____

*Other thoughts I have about this card:* _____

_____

_____

_____

_____

_____

_____

_____

_____

_____

_____

_____

# SIX OF SWORDS

*Keywords:* Transitions, travel, movement

*Meanings:* Transitions that go smoothly. New knowledge that helps one grow and move beyond current limitations. The lessening of difficulties. Travel in order to gain distance from difficulties. Detachment to better understand a situation. Healing.

*Reversed or weakly aspected:* More understanding of a situation is needed before it can change. Delay in departures, travel.

✧ ✧ ✧

THE WOMAN HAS ESCAPED HER ENEMIES and is sailing her boat to a better place. As she travels, she looks just as the goddess Isis did as she searched for Osiris along the Nile. With the woman are six swords she has gathered in her travels; these swords symbolize the new understanding and clarity she can use in her new life. Two dark birds fly above her. They are the harbingers of the Divine Feminine, flying and swooping just out of reach as they lead her toward wisdom and inner peace.

Even the most frustrating scenario will improve eventually if we work hard enough—the Six of Swords is a promise of this welcome release. Often all we need to do to transform a difficult situation is to gain understanding, so we may see it in a new light. The appearance of this card is a gentle reminder of the transforming powers of wisdom, which gives us the tools we need so we may move onto a better place.

*What troublesome situations would I like eased?* _____

_____

_____

_____

_____

*What can I do to move beyond it?* _____

_____

_____

_____

_____

*This card reminds me of the following:* _____

_____

_____

_____

_____

_____

_____

_____

*Other thoughts I have about this card:* _____

_____

_____

_____

_____

_____

_____

_____

_____

# SEVEN OF SWORDS

*Keywords:* Defense, vulnerability, caution

*Meanings:* Feeling vulnerable. The ability to defend oneself in a difficult situation. However, energy should not be placed in recriminations. Need for caution and examination. Be careful about using words that can be turned against you.

***Reversed or weakly aspected:*** Paranoia. Feeling defensive. Need for protection. Possible guilt.

❧ ❧ ❧

THE WOMAN ARRIVES IN A NEW LAND. Feeling the need for protection, she tries to carry seven swords with her. However only five will fit in her arms and even these are awkward to carry. With reluctance, she leaves two swords behind. As the woman nervously looks over her shoulder, she hopes they will not be used against her. She feels vulnerable—if only she possessed the strength of Isis she wouldn't need to carry all these swords.

The Seven of Swords suggests new situations in which we are uncertain who our friends are. Only time can show us the new lay of the land; in the meantime, we will have to be careful. Now is the time to examine our words, to consider our actions before it is too late to take them back. Any carelessness committed now may be regretted later, but as long as we are careful to act correctly we will be safe.

*What new situations make me vulnerable?*_____

_____

_____

_____

_____

*How can I protect myself?* _____

_____

_____

_____

_____

_____

*This card reminds me of the following:* _____

_____

_____

_____

_____

_____

_____

_____

*Other thoughts I have about this card:* _____

_____

_____

_____

_____

_____

_____

_____

_____

_____

# EIGHT OF SWORDS

*Keywords:* Deep depression, self-victimization, entrapment

*Meanings:* Inability to move. Depression that is incapacitating. Feeling victimized by others. Extreme sorrow that may be cause by oversensitivity. Feelings of rejection. Entrapped by emotions and sorrow.

***Reversed or weakly aspected:*** Things may not be as bad as they seem. Obsession with self and personal problems to the detriment of others. Problems that may come from within. Projecting negativity onto others. The lessening of obsessions.

✧ ✧ ✧

IN THE DISTANCE, an ominous storm gathers. Despite this threat, the woman collapses upon the desert sand too exhausted to continue any further. She feels as overwhelmed and entrapped as surely Osiris must have felt within his coffin. Eight swords surround her prostrate body, like the steel bars of a prison cage. Despite this unpleasant image, the woman would be able to see her way to freedom if she would only lift up her eyes. But she is too overwhelmed by depression to do so.

The disabling sorrow presented in the Eight of Swords is surely one of life's more unpleasant experiences. However a harsh solution is offered here: look beyond yourself. Often when unfortunate events occur it is too easy to fall into self-pity. We spend more time considering how victimized we are rather than looking for answers. This card is a wake-up call designed to mobilize us toward a better phase of life.

*Where do I feel entrapped in my life?* _____

_____

_____

_____

_____

*What actions can I take to free myself?* _____

_____

_____

_____

_____

_____

*This card reminds me of the following:* _____

_____

_____

_____

_____

_____

_____

_____

*Other thoughts I have about this card:* _____

_____

_____

_____

_____

_____

_____

_____

_____

# NINE OF SWORDS

**Keywords:** Anxiety, unresolved issues, insomnia

**Meanings:** Insomnia. Worries that keep one awake. An issue that needs to be looked at more closely; only then will it be transformed. Fear or nagging anxiety. Guilt. Psychic disturbances. Catharsis.

**Reversed or weakly aspected:** The fading away of these worries. Understanding. Someone close who is suffering from depression, anxiety, illness. The ability to transform pain into strength.

✤ ✤ ✤

THERE IS NO REST FOR THE WOMAN even in sleep—nightmares torment her. But while these dreams are painful, they do offer her an opportunity for catharsis. They bring up nagging worries that need to be examined, unresolved situations that need to be confronted. The symbol of the eye of Isis decorates the linens beneath the woman's pillow, revealing the divinely feminine wisdom awaiting her when she is ready. For only after she understands what these worries really mean will she be released from them.

The appearance of the Nine of Swords signifies the presence of thoughts that circle endlessly through our minds as they seek resolution. These obsessive concerns are often ignored during the day only to appear when we should be sleeping. This card offers the hope of release from this uncomfortable state of being.

*What do I obsess about in my life?*_____

_____

_____

_____

_____

*How do I resolve these bothersome thoughts?* _____

_____

_____

_____

_____

_____

*This card reminds me of the following:* _____

_____

_____

_____

_____

_____

*Other thoughts I have about this card:* _____

_____

_____

_____

_____

_____

_____

_____

_____

# TEN OF SWORDS

**Keywords:** Perfect understanding, endings, wisdom

**Meanings:** The perfection of wisdom, as expressed in the myth of Isis. Understanding gained after struggle. The ending of a difficult situation. Experience as the best teacher, for better and for worse. Sharing knowledge with others.

**Reversed or weakly aspected:** More needs to be considered before complete understanding can be gained. Overwhelmed by too much information. Getting lost in details—the inability to "see the forest for the trees."

ᛉ ᛉ ᛉ

FINALLY THE WOMAN ARRIVES at a vantage point where she can see the meeting of earth and sky. Several lightning bolts, symbolizing the shock of enlightenment, crack in the distant cloudy sky. Ten swords are interwoven into a graceful pattern in front of this intense scene. These swords symbolize the power of Isis, and offer magic to those who learn how to wield them. Those who master these swords will be able to transform all of life's difficulties into healing wisdom.

The Ten of Swords is the grand cumulation of the intense life lessons offered in the suit of swords. From here on, our struggles will be lessened, our road easier. Having gone through so much, we now possess the understanding that only experience can offer. The appearance of this card also suggests that it is time for us to share our wisdom with the world, since we have finally graduated from student to teacher.

*How do I feel I am wise?* _____

_____

_____

_____

_____

*What wisdom can I share with the world?* _____

_____

_____

_____

_____

_____

*This card reminds me of the following:* _____

_____

_____

_____

_____

_____

_____

_____

*Other thoughts I have about this card:* _____

_____

_____

_____

_____

_____

_____

_____

_____

_____

_____

# PRINCE OF SWORDS

**Keywords:** Messages, influence, articulation

**Meanings:** Articulation. News that brings sense to a situation. Messages, communications, often written. The ability to create influence and bring understanding, using the power of words. Someone who personifies this role.

**Reversed or weakly aspected:** Waiting for news. Feeling unable to stand up for oneself, inarticulate. Confusing messages.

✧ ✧ ✧

COURTLY BUT STRONG-WILLED, the Prince of Swords is able to use language as gracefully as he can wield his sword—his words bear no dishonesty or ambivalence. He is a trustworthy messenger presenting crucial information, often in the written form. A friend to writers, lawyers—those who wield words for a living—he offers clarity where there was confusion, wisdom where foolishness reigned.

The presence of the Prince of Swords in a tarot reading brings the power of the word to any area of life where it is needed. Verbal and written communications received now are especially important and will offer new clarity. If you are feeling a need for the forces personified in the Prince of Swords, the appearance of this card promises an increased mastery over language—the ability to be articulate, to find the words we need to create the life we want.

*In what way would I like to be more articulate?* _____

_____

_____

_____

_____

*How do I use language?* _____

_____

_____

_____

_____

_____

*This card reminds me of the following:* _____

_____

_____

_____

_____

_____

_____

*Other thoughts I have about this card:* _____

_____

_____

_____

_____

_____

_____

_____

_____

_____

_____

# PRINCESS OF SWORDS

**Keywords:** Decisiveness, clarity, defense

**Meanings:** The ability to move in an incisive way. Cutting through confusion. Being able to defend oneself brilliantly. Focus and clarity of understanding. A woman who symbolizes these forces.

**Reversed or weakly aspected:** Not understanding as much as one would like to. The desire to move, but feeling thwarted.

✧ ✧ ✧

HOLDING HER SWORD FOR SUPPORT rather than for defense, the Princess of Swords is able to cut her way through the swampy marsh of confusion. Strong-willed and confident, she is completely at one with her intentions. The contrary opinions of others do not deter her from following the path she knows she must take. The Princess of Swords is an unstoppable force; the strength of her focus gains her the admiration of many.

Often life requires us to defend ourselves with words, to present ourselves brilliantly. The Princess of Swords offers welcome proof that we can muster these abilities within ourselves if we need to. The appearance of this card suggests we will soon be experiencing the twin forces of clarity and incisiveness, as well as the talent to transform any difficult situation with these tools.

*How do I feel about defending myself?*_____

_____

_____

_____

_____

*Ways I have defended myself in the past:*_____

_____

_____

_____

_____

_____

*This card reminds me of the following:* _____

_____

_____

_____

_____

_____

_____

_____

*Other thoughts I have about this card:*_____

_____

_____

_____

_____

_____

_____

_____

_____

_____

_____

# KING OF SWORDS

*Keywords:* Authority, detachment, responsibility

*Meanings:* Calm authority and integrity. A helpful older man who won't sugarcoat words to protect others' feelings. Incisive intellect. Responsibility. High values that demand hard work.

*Reversed or weakly aspected:* Wanting authority to take over to avoid responsibility. Placing too much trust in the intellect. Being too critical.

✤ ✤ ✤

SITTING UPON HIS THRONE surrounded by lotus blossoms, the King of Swords is able to bring the wisdom and clarity of Isis to any situation. He is the authority able to look at a plan and recognize what is necessary and what can be cut away to strengthen it. Completely at home with his brilliance, he is a force to be admired and ultimately with which to be reckoned. The King of Swords symbolizes the high standards we must strive for in order to insure success in the rarified realm of the intellect.

Intelligence and education is often distrusted in our society, no doubt because we are intimidated by the authority inherent in it. The person who knows more than others is often the person in control of the situation. The appearance of the King of Swords in a tarot reading is an invitation to embrace these forces for ourselves. But it may not come easy—hard work and intense study will be involved. Often this card also represents an authority figure who personifies the incisive qualities explored in this card.

*In what situations do I feel like an authority?* _____

_____

_____

_____

*How do I feel about being an authority?* —————————

————————————————————————————

————————————————————————————

————————————————————————————

————————————————————————————

*This card reminds me of the following:* ——————————

————————————————————————————

————————————————————————————

————————————————————————————

————————————————————————————

————————————————————————————

*Other thoughts I have about this card:* ——————————

————————————————————————————

————————————————————————————

————————————————————————————

————————————————————————————

————————————————————————————

————————————————————————————

————————————————————————————

# QUEEN OF SWORDS

**Keywords:** Brilliance, honesty, clarity

**Meanings:** Dazzling intellect. Perfect understanding. The ability to clarify through language. Brilliance in writing, speaking or anything else transmitted with words. An older woman who has these qualities.

**Reversed or weakly aspected:** May symbolize loss or wounds. Despite good intentions, sharp words wound people and affect relationships. Allowing intellect to rule over the heart detrimentally. Psychological manipulation.

✥ ✥ ✥

WEARING A HEADPIECE that bears the symbol of Isis, the Queen of Swords should be treated with the highest respect. She is the ideal woman to consult when troubled with problems—she will tell it like it is, even to the point of sometimes being a little harsh. Strong and dazzlingly brilliant, the Queen of Swords rules over all aspects of intellectual understanding. She symbolizes the perfect understanding of the Divine Feminine that can be gained through experiences both happy and painful.

We all know someone who bears the qualities of the Queen of Swords: brilliant, incisive, powerful, even intimidating. The presence of this card dares us to develop these qualities in ourselves. This challenge can be frightening to those who believe their powers only come through pleasing others. As we strengthen ourselves, we may lose those who do not like our new honesty and confidence.

*Where can I be more powerful in my life?*_____

_____

_____

_____

_____

*How would this change me?* _____

_____

_____

_____

_____

_____

*This card reminds me of the following:* _____

_____

_____

_____

_____

_____

_____

_____

*Other thoughts I have about this card:* _____

_____

_____

_____

_____

_____

_____

_____

_____

_____

_____

_____

ACE
PENTACLES

TWO
PENTACLES

THREE
PENTACLES

FOUR
PENTACLES

QUEEN
PENTACLES

FIVE
PENTACLES

KING
PENTACLES

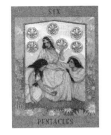

SIX
PENTACLES

PRINCESS
PENTACLES

SEVEN
PENTACLES

PRINCE
PENTACLES

TEN
PENTACLES

NINE
PENTACLES

EIGHT
PENTACLES

*Chapter Five:*
# THE MINOR ARCANA

The Suit of Pentacles

## *Element: Earth, gold*
## *Corresponds to Fortune, Major Arcana card number 10*

The suit of pentacles is associated with Lakshmi, the Hindu goddess of fortune and prosperity. Pentacles, as shiny and precious as the sparkling jewels of which Lakshmi is so fond, symbolize the riches contained within the earth that are ours for the taking once we learn how to mine them.

The suit of pentacles tells the story of the earth's bounty, symbolized in so many societies as a generous earth goddess fully capable of nurturing all of her inhabitants. Lakshmi, the Hindu personification of this fertile, prosperous and distinctly feminine force, is well-loved to this day by many people for these very qualities. Perhaps in support of these beliefs, this goddess is often depicted upon coins as bright as the fortune she offers those who honor her.

When staves appear in a tarot reading, they represent the grand harvest that arrives only after we undergo the lessons of the three previous suits: cups water the seed of inspiration initially planted by the Divine Feminine; staves are the first growth that sprout vigorously from the fertile earth thanks to the sun's encouragement; and swords prune staves for the sake of growth. Finally, in the suit of pentacles, the reinvigorated tree bears seeded fruit so the cycle may start anew.

### THE MYTH OF LAKSHMI ✧ ✧ ✧

In Hindu mythology, the goddess Lakshmi is believed to represent all that is feminine while her god consort, Vishnu, represents all that is masculine. Lakshmi was created when Vishnu churned the wondrous Ocean of Milk. She magically appeared from its creamy depths seated upon a lotus flower throne with a lotus blossom crown upon her pale brow, (the lotus symbolizing her divinity). Vishnu immediately fell in love with this new goddess, and in time they had a son named Kama. In the Hindu tradition, Kama is still honored as the god of romantic love .

As the goddess of earthly prosperity, Lakshmi is thought to be attracted to sparkling jewels, much like the riches she bestows upon her faithful worshippers. Not surprisingly, some people believe that Lakshmi lives in the sky with the stars, the most beautiful jewels of all. Every year in November, on the night of the new moon—when the sky is at its darkest and the stars their brightest—a festival called Divali is celebrated in her honor. Indian women clean their homes and hang tiny lanterns as bright as diamonds, hoping to attract Lakshmi's notice so they may win her favor for the coming year.

An Overview of the Suit of Pentacles, the Path of Lakshmi ♧ ♧ ♧

| MINOR ARCANA CARD | KEY WORDS |
| --- | --- |
| Ace of Pentacles | *fertility, generosity, prosperity* |
| Two of Pentacles | *grace, expansion, juggling, activity* |
| Three of Pentacles | *building, material manifestation, construction* |
| Four of Pentacles | *wealth, stability, security, inheritance* |
| Five of Pentacles | *poverty, sterility, insecurity, spiritual richness* |
| Six of Pentacles | *generosity, helping others, charity* |
| Seven of Pentacles | *waiting, expectations, nurturing* |
| Eight of Pentacles | *talent, compensation, honorable work* |
| Nine of Pentacles | *luxury, prosperity, pleasure, fertility* |
| Ten of Pentacles | *cumulation, prosperity, expansion* |
| Prince of Pentacles | *business ideas, messages, education* |
| Princess of Pentacles | *opportunities, hard work, development* |
| King of Pentacles | *steadfastness, wealth creation, riches* |
| Queen of Pentacles | *fertility, prosperity, beauty* |

# ACE OF PENTACLES

**Keywords:** Fertility, generosity, prosperity

**Meanings:** The Divine Feminine's purest evocation of prosperity, fertility and generosity. The beginning of a new phase of life that promises the good fortune of Lakshmi. Attainment of material goals as well as contentment in personal life. Fertility. Pleasures of the material world.

**Reversed or weakly aspected:** A desire to reap the fruits of labor. Elusive success. Need to examine how one undermines oneself.

✤ ✤ ✤

WITHIN AN ENCHANTED LANDSCAPE sprinkled with gold flowers, a lush tree bears a fantastic fruit—a single golden coin. This ornately decorated coin symbolizes the most bountiful manifestation of the Divine Feminine upon earth. It bears the image of a pentacle, the ancient five-pointed star that is a magical symbol of wisdom. The pentacle's five connected sides are believed to reveal the never ending, always flowing force of the Divine Feminine. Engraved around the pentacle is an image of a lotus, which represents the joyful birth of Lakshmi, the goddess of earthly prosperity and the enlightenment she offers.

The Ace of Pentacles suggests the beginning of the grand harvest symbolized by this suit. After traveling the paths offered in the suits of cups, staves and swords, we are now ready to reap the rewards of all the lessons we have mastered. A deep experience of prosperity is now ours, if we are willing to accept these bounties.

*Where do I feel prosperity in my life?* _____

_____

_____

_____

*How do I feel blessed?*_____

_____

_____

_____

_____

_____

*This card reminds me of the following:* _____

_____

_____

_____

_____

_____

_____

_____

*Other thoughts I have about this card:*_____

_____

_____

_____

_____

_____

_____

_____

_____

_____

_____

# TWO OF PENTACLES

**Keywords:** Grace, activity, juggling, expansion

**Meanings:** The ability to juggle several situations at once—jobs, opportunities, ideas. Balance between the earthly and the spiritual worlds. Grace and bounty. Commerce and expansion.

**Reversed or weakly aspected:** Taking on too much for now. Feeling overwhelmed by demands. Time to concentrate on one thing at a time; do this well before you expand. Overcommitting oneself.

✥ ✥ ✥

BY THE SEA, the woman juggles two pentacles gracefully. She is so completely focused upon her act, so undistracted by outside influences, that she does not drop them as they swirl in mid-air. Around her feet, which are clad in green—the color of the earth—flows the incoming tide. This symbolizes the perfect balance she holds within herself. Around the woman blows a gentle but persistent wind, representing the twin forces of movement and change.

Juggling is a given in many people's lives. How else can we accept the bounty of blessings and responsibilities offered to us? There is simply not enough time to do everything we'd like—family, creativity, business, friends—so juggle we must. The presence of the Two of Pentacles suggests that you are handling this complicated life so well that more opportunities are coming your way. Be prepared to continue this balancing act!

*What do I juggle in my life?* _____

_____

_____

_____

*What new opportunities would I like?* _____

_____

_____

_____

_____

_____

*This card reminds me of the following:* _____

_____

_____

_____

_____

_____

_____

*Other thoughts I have about this card:* _____

_____

_____

_____

_____

_____

_____

_____

_____

_____

# THREE OF PENTACLES

**Keywords:** Building, material manifestation, construction

**Meanings:** Constructive building of career, relationships, home. Alchemy or turning base energy into gold. The ability to transform talents into material goods or business success. Cooperating with others to create such a venture.

**Reversed or weakly aspected:** Need to develop one's talents before entering the marketplace. Recheck plans for expansion—are they practical? Are they appropriate for your abilities? Time for a reality check from those who may be more experienced.

✤ ✤ ✤

THE WOMAN ARRIVES at a palatial building, the most beautiful she has ever seen. A golden light reveals three magnificent pentacles suspended within one of the building's bell-shaped roofs. The woman can tell that this palace is the cumulation of a great deal of hard work and talent; much material good and constructive planning has gone into creating it. She also knows it symbolizes the goals that she can reach if she dedicates herself and draws upon the wisdom of Lakshmi.

The appearance of the Three of Pentacles in a tarot reading offers the expansive message that our most beloved plans can become reality. All we need to do is plan carefully and build, never ceasing in our labors until our goals are before us. Often this card presents us with the vision needed to spur us into action—to create this vision of heaven on earth, we may require helpers and even additional education.

*What would I like to build in my life?* _____

_____

_____

_____

_____

*What tools do I need to do so?*_____

_____

_____

_____

_____

_____

_____

*This card reminds me of the following:* _____

_____

_____

_____

_____

_____

_____

_____

_____

*Other thoughts I have about this card:*_____

_____

_____

_____

_____

_____

_____

_____

_____

_____

_____

# FOUR OF PENTACLES

**Keywords:** Wealth, inheritance, stability, security

**Meanings:** Wealth and prosperity. Stability of material forces in one's life. Holding onto worldly goods. A family inheritance—this could be a talent handed down, money, land or a quality that adds richness to life. Self-satisfaction.

**Reversed or weakly aspected:** Possibility of being miserly with wealth, talents. Conversely, being an overly generous spendthrift. Need to conserve and protect resources. Envy of others.

✤ ✤ ✤

WELL PLEASED WITH HERSELF, the woman rests in a peaceful meadow surrounded by distant purple mountains; these mountains symbolize spiritual enlightenment and the verdant meadow, earthly manifestation. She is draped in richly embroidered robes and laden with gold and jewels—she is as glittering with wealth as the goddess Lakshmi herself. Surrounded by four magnificent pentacles, the woman is the very epitome of luxury and prosperity.

The Four of Pentacles presents us with an enticing vision of material stability. The riches depicted in this card are the true manifestation of earthly prosperity: talents, money, land, security and more. Because we own so much, we are now able to share our wealth with the world.

*Where do I feel wealthy in my life?* _____

_____

_____

_____

_____

*What beliefs do I hold about wealth?* _____

_____

_____

_____

_____

_____

*This card reminds me of the following:* _____

_____

_____

_____

_____

_____

_____

_____

_____

*Other thoughts I have about this card:* _____

_____

_____

_____

_____

_____

_____

_____

_____

_____

# FIVE OF PENTACLES

**Keywords:** Poverty, sterility, insecurity, spiritual richness

**Meanings:** An experience of poverty that forces one to look within for greater resources. This poverty may be personified as a lack of wealth or in a sense of emotional sterility. Spiritual impoverishment. Feeling deprived. Insecurity.

**Reversed or weakly aspected:** These feelings are transitory. Have faith in the future—a more prosperous phase of life is on its way. The ability to make the best of a difficult situation.

❧ ❧ ❧

TWO BEGGARS WRAPPED IN RAGS wander through a snowy landscape in search of support. The snow and winds are so fierce that one of the women covers her face for protection against the harsh cold. She wonders if she will ever again feel warmth, security and prosperity—all the comforting things she associates with the goddess Lakshmi. The other woman tries not to fret; instead, she looks up at the snow and is moved by its pure, transcendent beauty.

The appearance of the Five of Pentacles in a reading dares us to examine our most deeply held beliefs about poverty, to reconsider what we believe we lack in lives. During this process we may be confronted with feelings of deprivation that shake us to our very core. As uncomfortable as these emotions are, they do offer an opportunity to learn what truly nurtures us.

*Where do I feel poor in my life?* _____

_____

_____

_____

_____

*How do I handle feelings of deprivation?* _____

_____

_____

_____

_____

_____

*This card reminds me of the following:* _____

_____

_____

_____

_____

_____

_____

_____

*Other thoughts I have about this card:* _____

_____

_____

_____

_____

_____

_____

_____

_____

_____

_____

# SIX OF PENTACLES

**Keywords:** Generosity, helping others, charity

**Meanings:** True generosity and philanthropy. Sharing talents with the world and hoping they'll be received gracefully. Trusting in the prosperity of the universe. Helping others who are less fortunate without expectations.

**Reversed or weakly aspected:** Jealousy or envy from those less fortunate. Not giving with a pure heart. Need for appreciation. Using wealth to manipulate others.

✧ ✧ ✧

THE TWO BEGGARS ENCOUNTER THE WOMAN, who is still dressed in her luxurious jewels and prosperous clothes. Moved by their plight, she decides to share her wealth with them. Fortunately, the woman is so rich that the act of giving only increases her riches. However, the dynamic of giving and receiving makes her uncomfortable since it implies a debt on the part of the beggars. She understands that true generosity bears no expectations of return.

True generosity is a force that only enriches the giver—just as true wealth can never be taken away from us. The Six of Pentacles is a gentle reminder of the immeasurable prosperity of the Divine Feminine. This card also serves us notice that we are put upon this earth to share our wealth in whatever form we possess it.

*When have I been generous to others?* _____

_____

_____

_____

_____

*How do I feel about philanthropy?* _____

_____

_____

_____

_____

_____

*This card reminds me of the following:* _____

_____

_____

_____

_____

_____

_____

_____

*Other thoughts I have about this card:* _____

_____

_____

_____

_____

_____

_____

_____

_____

_____

# SEVEN OF PENTACLES

**Keywords:** Waiting, expectations, nurturing

**Meanings:** Expectations of reward or money. Waiting for a harvest of a creative project, personal relationship or any venture in which time and work are invested. Tending your "garden." Nurturing others.

**Reversed or weakly aspected:** Impatience. Insecurity about whether the reward received for the work rendered will be worth it. Need to work harder to create prosperity.

✢ ✢ ✢

IN HOPES OF CREATING EVEN MORE PROSPERITY, the woman tends a tree. She weeds around its roots and prunes its heavy boughs so it may grow better. As she waits for its fruit to ripen, she thinks back about her hard work. The fruit is symbolized here by the seven golden pentacles suspended upon its strong branches. The woman looks forward to enjoying the richly deserved harvest she has nurtured for so long.

We have all experienced the hard work and expectations that go into any long term project. The Seven of Pentacles depicts the anticipation as we wait: the hopes, the dreams, the excitement. The appearance of this card offers the optimistic message that we will not have to wait for much longer, soon our harvest will come to fruition.

*Where am I waiting for harvest in my life?* _____

_____

_____

_____

_____

_____

*How have I nurtured this project?*_____

_____

_____

_____

_____

_____

_____

*This card reminds me of the following:*_____

_____

_____

_____

_____

_____

_____

_____

_____

*Other thoughts I have about this card:*_____

_____

_____

_____

_____

_____

_____

_____

_____

_____

_____

_____

# EIGHT OF PENTACLES

**Keywords:** Talent, compensation, honorable work

**Meanings:** Creative work. Fair payment for hard work. Meeting deadlines. Developing talents for the marketplace. Working with integrity and discipline. The appearance of this card in a reading for an artist or craftsperson is an affirmation of skill and talent.

**Reversed or weakly aspected:** Avoiding work. Need to bring talents to the next level—perhaps taking time for vocational education. Unhappiness with money received for work done. Involvement in "get rich quick" schemes to avoid hard labor.

✤ ✤ ✤

THE WOMAN DECIDES TO EXPRESS HER ARTISTRY by painting a gold pentacle upon a silk canvas. As she works, she loses herself in creativity's flow. She feels blessed as she draws upon the talents given to her by the Divine Feminine. An arc of seven pentacles appears above her head, like a golden rainbow depicting the material rewards of Lakshmi. This vision symbolizes the golden circle of contentment the woman has created with her focused and inspired labor.

The appearance of the Eight of Pentacles in an artisan's tarot reading is a welcome sight. It offers acknowledgement of talent, hard work and, perhaps most importantly, fair payment. Expect to find great satisfaction in any work undertaken at this time. If you are feeling less than enthralled with your career, this card offers an ideal for which to aim. Perhaps it is time to develop the skills necessary to create your dream job.

*What would be my ideal job?* _____

_____

_____

_____

*How can I create greater satisfaction at work?*_____

_____

_____

_____

_____

_____

*This card reminds me of the following:* _____

_____

_____

_____

_____

_____

_____

_____

*Other thoughts I have about this card:*_____

_____

_____

_____

_____

_____

_____

_____

_____

_____

_____

# NINE OF PENTACLES

*Keywords:* Luxury, prosperity, pleasure, fertility

*Meanings:* Pleasure or sensuality. Feeling blessed by life. Enjoying the fruits of one's labors. Material prosperity—now that this has been accomplished, perhaps it is time to create a family. Fertility and luxury.

*Reversed or weakly aspected:* Overindulgence in material pleasures, perhaps to the point of compromising financial stability. Guilt over possessing so much; inability to enjoy it. Fear of other's envy.

✧ ✧ ✧

AFTER BRINGING HER HARD WORK TO THE MARKETPLACE, the woman arrives at an enchanted garden. Overflowing with perfumed flowers, jasmine trees and singing birds, she luxuriates in all the beauty she has worked so hard to create. Nine golden pentacles appear around her like fruit upon the vine of earthly delights. These pentacles symbolize the blessings of Lakshmi and the Divine Feminine.

The vision of idyllic repose and beauty presented in this scene is one that many yearn to experience in their lifetime. Within ourselves, we all bear the ability to create this manifestation of heaven upon earth. The Nine of Pentacles promises us the fruits of our labor. The appearance of this card suggests that this serene sanctuary may be closer than we realize, for we have worked hard; we are ready for our well-deserved reward.

*What would my ideal environment be like?* _____

_____

_____

_____

_____

Describe your ideal life: _____

_____

_____

_____

_____

_____

This card reminds me of the following: _____

_____

_____

_____

_____

_____

_____

_____

Other thoughts I have about this card: _____

_____

_____

_____

_____

_____

_____

_____

_____

# TEN OF PENTACLES

*Keywords:* Cumulation, prosperity, expansion

*Meanings:* Great satisfaction. Prosperity and the construction of a home that reflects this state. Creating a family to share wealth with. The successful cumulation of business plans. Expansion. An inheritance. Joy and pleasure.

*Reversed or weakly aspected:* Discontent at home or difficulties with family relationships. Wanting more prosperity, but uncertain how to achieve it. Elusive success on the material plane.

✤ ✤ ✤

THE ENCHANTED GARDEN LEADS THE WOMAN to a gateway framing a lush verdant landscape. Ten pentacles glitter there within the gateway's ornate carving and upon a verdant tree. They depict the expansive nature of the world, the inherent beauty surrounding us—all the wonderful things sacred to Lakshmi, goddess of prosperity.

The Ten of Pentacles depicts the innate goodness of the world surrounding us. It is here that the suit of pentacles is expressed at its most expansive and life-affirming. It is here that there is more than enough bounty for all to enjoy. The celebration expressed in this card is the successful cumulation of the great journey traveled through the three preceding suits of cups, staves and swords—we have now arrived at a place of plenty.

*Where do I find bounty in my life?* _____

_____

_____

_____

_____

_____

*How can life be an expansive experience?* _____

_____

_____

_____

_____

_____

*This card reminds me of the following:* _____

_____

_____

_____

_____

_____

_____

_____

*Other thoughts I have about this card:* _____

_____

_____

_____

_____

_____

_____

_____

_____

_____

# PRINCE OF PENTACLES

**Keywords:** Business ideas, money, messages, education

**Meanings:** Gaining the knowledge necessary to make an idea a reality. Education. Business ideas, deals. Practical planning. Mail or messages that bring possibilities for expansion. Money on the way. Business opportunities.

**Reversed or weakly aspected:** Too much time thinking, not enough doing. Business deals that need to be examined closely. Waiting for money, business news. Unrealistic planning.

✦ ✦ ✦

GARBED IN LUXURIOUSLY EMBROIDERED SILKS, jewels, and gold, the Prince of Pentacles holds a single pentacle in his hands. Practical and grounded, this young man is surprisingly mature for his few years. He is not afraid to work hard to manifest the prosperity so loved by Lakshmi. When not working, he is a bringer of messages and ideas, and is able to show where businesses can expand and when they can harvest.

Every new idea could use some grounding. The Prince of Pentacles offers a pragmatic counterbalance to new ventures when our excitement makes it easy to lose sight of reality. His steady energy presents knowledge needed to bring a plan to fruition as well as the money to get them started. Any communications or opportunities received now will bear the mark of these valuable forces—take them seriously.

*What ideas do I have that need grounding?* _____

_____

_____

_____

_____

*How can I bring them to fruition?*_____

_____

_____

_____

_____

_____

*This card reminds me of the following:* _____

_____

_____

_____

_____

_____

_____

*Other thoughts I have about this card:*_____

_____

_____

_____

_____

_____

_____

_____

_____

_____

# PRINCESS OF PENTACLES

**Keywords:** Opportunities, hard work, development

**Meanings:** The ability, hard work and wisdom necessary to create growth, beauty. Movement in this direction. The ability to work hard to create prosperity. Taking care of the self on the material level and enjoying the pleasures associated with this. A woman personifying these forces.

**Reversed or weakly aspected:** Inertia or laziness. Not taking action or responsibilities. Over-sensuality. Wanting to get something for nothing—credit where no credit is due.

✧✧✧

SEDUCTIVE AND SWEETLY PERFUMED, the Princess of Pentacles promises all of life's robust riches. Her presence reminds others of the hard work and clear focus necessary to manifest them. To possess these, desire is not enough—constructive action must be taken. The Princess of Pentacles, as a personification of the constructive, active forces of Lakshmi, is able to provide the push we need to create our own vision of heaven upon earth.

Prosperity is all about us—the appearance of the Princess of Pentacles in a tarot reading suggests that these lush, bountiful and generous forces now surround us. If you are feeling a sense of deprivation, this card suggests that this phase will not continue for much longer. As long as you work hard, movement to a more prosperous time of life is assured—all you need to do is prepare the ground for your flowering.

*Where would I like more prosperity?* _____

_____

_____

_____

_____

*How can I prepare myself to receive it?* _____

_____

_____

_____

_____

_____

*This card reminds me of the following:* _____

_____

_____

_____

_____

_____

_____

_____

_____

*Other thoughts I have about this card:* _____

_____

_____

_____

_____

_____

_____

_____

_____

_____

_____

_____

# KING OF PENTACLES

*Keywords:* Steadfastness, wealth creation, riches

*Meanings:* The forces of worldly prosperity. The ability to create wealth. Real estate transactions. Investments—financial or emotional. Steadfast. Someone who personifies these forces.

*Reversed or weakly aspected:* Unstable, pie-in-the-sky business deals. Need to be more realistic. Involvement with people who may promise more than they are able to deliver. The need for stability and discipline in life.

✧ ✧ ✧

SURROUNDED BY THE BEST the earth has to offer, the King of Pentacles is a stabilizing force with the ability to bring business and real estate deals to completion. Often he is the moneyman behind the scenes, the nurturing authority whose steadfast integrity inspires others as they work. His practical wisdom is an inspiration to all who would own the wealth promised by the goddess Lakshmi.

The King of Pentacles is the personification of worldly prosperity: real estate, money, investments. His presence in any tarot reading suggests the physical manifestation of the Divine Feminine in her most concrete form. This card invites us to create this wealth for ourselves so that we may enjoy the best that the material world offers.

*What material goods would I like to own?* _____

_____

_____

_____

_____

*How can I gain them?* _____

_____

_____

_____

_____

_____

*This card reminds me of the following?* _____

_____

_____

_____

_____

_____

_____

_____

*Other thoughts I have about this card:* _____

_____

_____

_____

_____

_____

_____

_____

_____

_____

# QUEEN OF PENTACLES

*Keywords:* Fertility, prosperity, beauty

*Meanings:* Creating prosperity and harmony. Beauty, wealth, the home. Fertility, possibly parenthood. Regality. Warmth and affection. Love. Happy harmonious home. A woman who is nurturing and accepting.

*Reversed or weakly aspected:* Need to ground oneself. Perhaps an overmaterialistic orientation to life. Disappointment in the home or lack of focus upon.

✦ ✦ ✦

THE QUEEN OF PENTACLES is the physical manifestation of the fertile life force of the Divine Feminine. The jewels she wears and the pentacle posed upon her lap show that she possesses all the riches of the physical world. She offers unlimited possibilities for wealth and happiness. This expansive older woman possesses the joyful talent to create heaven upon earth for all who honor her influence. The archetypal earth mother, the Queen of Pentacles brings harmony and beauty to any area of life.

We all hold within ourselves the potential to experience everything we have ever desired. Our fondest hopes for our material life are personified in the Queen of Pentacles. The appearance of this card suggests that a new phase of existence is beginning where we will be encouraged to fulfill all we have ever dreamed of—we will be nurtured by the prosperous, earthly forces of the Divine Feminine.

*What is my fondest dream for my life?* _____

_____

_____

_____

_____

*How can I nurture this dream?* _____

_____

_____

_____

_____

_____

_____

*This card reminds me of the following:* _____

_____

_____

_____

_____

_____

_____

_____

*Other thoughts I have about this card:* _____

_____

_____

_____

_____

_____

_____

_____

_____

_____

_____

_____

O ~ BEGINNINGS

TARA

I ~ MAGIC

ISIS

II ~ WISDOM

SARASVATI

III ~ FERTILITY

ESTSANATLEHI

IV ~ POWER

FREYJA

V ~ TRADITION

JUNO

XXI ~ THE WORLD

GAIA

VI ~ LOVE

VENUS

XX ~ JUDGMENT

GWENHWYFAR

VII ~ MOVEMENT

RHIANNON

XIX ~ THE SUN

THE ZORYA

VIII ~ JUSTICE

ATHENA

XVIII ~ THE MOON

DIANA

IX ~ CONTEMPLATION

CHANG O

XVII ~ THE STAR

INANNA

X ~ FORTUNE

LAKSHMI

XVI ~ OPPRESSION

THE WAWALAK

XV ~ TEMPTATION

NYAI LORO KIDUL

XIV ~ BALANCE

YEMANA

XIII ~ TRANSFORMATION

UKEMOCHI

XII ~ SACRIFICE

KUAN YIN

XI ~ STRENGTH

OYA

*Chapter Six:*

# TAROT SPREADS

*The Past/Present/Future Spread*
*The Burning Question*
*The Beginnings Tree*
*The Celtic Cross*
*The Relationship Cross*
*The Circle of Strength*

The tarot has been used for many years by people striving to better understand their life journey. In several of my books, I've written of the challenge of acknowledging the divine within ourselves. I hope that *The Goddess Tarot* can be used as a tool for this great quest.

Unlike *The Goddess Tarot* book, the emphasis in *The Goddess Tarot Workbook* is upon reading the Goddess Tarot for yourself—rather than as a predictive act for the benefit of others. This is not meant to start a debate over which way is more worthy; it only reflects the orientation of this workbook, whose main goal is to use these cards as a tool for self-knowledge. For those mainly interested in using the Goddess Tarot to read for friends and family, I hope you will take comfort in my belief that the awareness gained from reading for yourself will only heighten your abilities to read for others.

For those who fear the tarot or invest it with predictive powers outside themselves, rest easy. I believe that tarot readings cannot tell you what you do not already know, even if you are unwilling to accept this knowledge at this time. A good tarot reading should be an adventure into truth seeking rather than soothsaying. The beauty of tarot is that it presents the information in a new form—like another opinion, but one without a vested interest.

Most people give tarot readings by placing a number of cards into a pattern called a tarot spread. Each card position within the spread represents an area of the question to be explored during the reading. In this section of *The Goddess Tarot Workbook*, six tarot spreads are presented along with detailed instructions on how to use them. Each of these spreads pertains to a particular area of life. They are also arranged in order of difficulty—from simplest to the most complex—thus allowing you to comfortably progress as you gain confidence and skill. Several pages of blank tarot spread forms (for you to record your readings) follow each tarot spread description.

Another helpful exercise I recommend is to write your tarot readings in a journal. Often the conscious act of preserving this information will jog the subconscious into making connections previously overlooked. If you'd like, you can photocopy extra blank tarot spread forms from this workbook and place them into a ring bound notebook, one way to create a tarot journal for saving your Goddess Tarot readings.

As you continue working with the Goddess Tarot, please feel free to take only what rings true to your personal experiences and leave behind what doesn't. Personalize what remains so that it has as much meaning as it can for you. But most importantly, honor your intuition—it is here that the quiet wisdom of the Divine Feminine often speaks loudest to those who are willing to listen.

PREPARING FOR A TAROT READING ❦ ❦ ❦

Before the start of tarot reading, a question needs to be decided upon. How to phrase this question is an important consideration. Generally, questions that receive the best responses are those which are posed with the greatest thought and clarity of intention. Choose your words carefully; wording is important and implies an awareness of the responsibility involved.

Next, decide upon the tarot spread to use and choose the appropriate number of cards. Cards are usually chosen for a tarot reading by shuffling the cards a preordained number of times (to assure randomness) and cutting the deck.

Another thing to consider before you choose your cards is whether you wish to include reversed (or upside-down) cards in your readings. These can be created by turning some of the cards around as you shuffle. Some people believe that reversed cards add another dimension of clarity to readings; these cards serve as focal points, showing where energy may be blocked in a situation or special attention needed. Others feel that all the information needed to create a full picture is already contained within the seventy-eight cards of the tarot—reversed cards just muddy the water. Again, this is up to you.

However you decide to proceed, it is important to focus yourself before the actual reading. A simple ritual, such as lighting a candle or closing your eyes for a moment, can help create a properly receptive atmosphere for the information about to be shared by the cards.

Whichever tarot spread you decide to use, as you look over the cards chosen for your reading, try to think of each card as a chapter in a story you are telling. What do the pictures tell you? How can this story be changed, if change is wanted? And what lesson is being taught, what challenge offered?

Also take note of the proximity and position of a card. See if there is a preponderance of any one suit or arcana. Personal feelings or memories may surface as you gaze at the images before you—they are important and should be noted as well, for they add a level of emotional richness that no book definition can provide.

Most of the time you will probably find your readings to be astonishingly clear, requiring only a simple examination to let its full picture unfold. If the meaning of a tarot reading seems mysterious, perhaps the situation itself is confused. It may not be the correct time for the the information to be given—wait a little while before trying again. Finally, remember that the future is fluid and is affected by our actions in the present.

# THE PAST/PRESENT/FUTURE SPREAD

THE PAST/PRESENT/FUTURE SPREAD, the first tarot spread offered here, offers a wonderfully accessible introduction to tarot card reading for the newcomer to this art. This tarot spread is particularly suited for simple questions that do not require a great deal of examination. It's also great when you're short on time but need a quick overview of a situation. Allow yourself ten minutes for this reading.

Choose four cards at random from your deck, concentrating upon your question as you do so. Lay them out as shown in the diagram. Each card is placed face down; turn up one at a time to examine it:

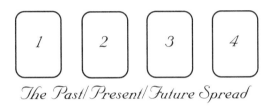

*The Past/Present/Future Spread*

*Card 1:* This card represents the past, or foundation, of the situation being considered.

*Card 2:* The present, or the situation as it stands now.

*Card 3:* The possible future, if things continue as they are now. Remember, the future can be influenced by our attitudes, actions and intentions.

*Card 4:* The final card offers the overall message, or lesson, of the spread, summing up everything examined so far. Often this card can offer us possible ways to proceed if we have any questions about what we should do.

Date of Reading:_____

Card 1:_____    Card 3:_____

Card 2:_____    Card 4:_____

*My question:*_____

_____

_____

*The first thing I observed about the cards I chose:*_____

_____

_____

_____

*My thoughts about this reading:* _____

_____

_____

_____

_____

_____

_____

_____

Date of Reading:_____

Card 1:_____     Card 3:_____

Card 2:_____     Card 4:_____

*My question:*_____

_____

_____

*The first thing I observed about the cards I chose:*_____

_____

_____

_____

*My thoughts about this reading:*_____

_____

_____

_____

_____

_____

_____

_____

Date of Reading:_____

| | | | |
|---|---|---|---|
| 1 | 2 | 3 | 4 |

Card 1:_____     Card 3:_____

Card 2:_____     Card 4:_____

*My question:*_____

_____

_____

*The first thing I observed about the cards I chose:*_____

_____

_____

_____

*My thoughts about this reading:*_____

_____

_____

_____

_____

_____

_____

_____

_____

Date of Reading:_____

Card 1:_____    Card 3:_____

Card 2:_____    Card 4:_____

*My question:*_____

_____

_____

*The first thing I observed about the cards I chose:*_____

_____

_____

_____

*My thoughts about this reading:*_____

_____

_____

_____

_____

_____

_____

_____

_____

# THE BURNING QUESTION

DEVELOPED BY PROFESSIONAL TAROT READER Laura Mead-Desmet of www.atasteoftarot.com, this tarot layout is slightly more complex than the Past/Present/Future spread. It's for those times when you have a specific question that has to be addressed immediately—a burning question. Hence the name for this spread. A card symbolizing the question is placed at the center of the spread with the remaining six cards placed around it, suggesting the shape of a flame as it clings to an object that consumes it.

Take a moment to calm your mind and concentrate on your burning question. Then shuffle the deck and choose seven cards at random. Place them as shown in the diagram:

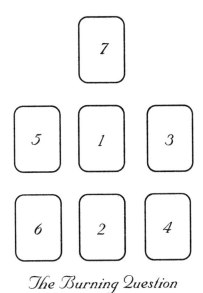

*The Burning Question*

*Card 1:* The question. This card sums up the overall situation for which you are asking guidance.

*Card 2:* Obstacles or supporting influences in reference to this question.

*Cards 3 and 4:* Both of these cards refer to the hopes and fears, worries and desires concerning your question. These two cards can be seen as one card telling about worries/fears and one about hopes/desires. Or they both can speak to only one aspect—just worries or just hopes.

*Cards 5 and 6:* These cards offer additional information about your question—suggestions and options to consider before you decide how to proceed.

*Card 7:* Possible outcome. Based on what has gone before, this is where your situation is heading if things continue as they have.

Date of Reading:_____

```
            ┌─────┐
            │     │
            │  7  │
            │     │
            └─────┘

  ┌─────┐   ┌─────┐   ┌─────┐
  │     │   │     │   │     │
  │  5  │   │  1  │   │  3  │
  │     │   │     │   │     │
  └─────┘   └─────┘   └─────┘

  ┌─────┐   ┌─────┐   ┌─────┐
  │     │   │     │   │     │
  │  6  │   │  2  │   │  4  │
  │     │   │     │   │     │
  └─────┘   └─────┘   └─────┘
```

Card 1:_____            Card 4:_____

Card 2:_____            Card 5:_____

Card 3:_____            Card 6:_____

Card 7:_____

*My question:*_____

_____

_____

*The first thing I observed about the cards I chose:*_____

_____

_____

_____

*My thoughts about this reading:*_____

Date of Reading: _____

```
                            ┌───────┐
                            │       │
                            │   7   │
                            │       │
                            └───────┘

        ┌───────┐       ┌───────┐       ┌───────┐
        │       │       │       │       │       │
        │   5   │       │   1   │       │   3   │
        │       │       │       │       │       │
        └───────┘       └───────┘       └───────┘

        ┌───────┐       ┌───────┐       ┌───────┐
        │       │       │       │       │       │
        │   6   │       │   2   │       │   4   │
        │       │       │       │       │       │
        └───────┘       └───────┘       └───────┘
```

Card 1: _____          Card 4: _____

Card 2: _____          Card 5: _____

Card 3: _____          Card 6: _____

Card 7: _____

*My question:* _____

_____

_____

*The first thing I observed about the cards I chose:* _____

_____

_____

_____

*My thoughts about this reading:* _____

_____

_____

_____

_____

_____

_____

_____

_____

_____

_____

_____

_____

_____

_____

_____

_____

_____

_____

_____

_____

_____

_____

_____

_____

_____

_____

_____

_____

_____

_____

Date of Reading:_____

Card 1:_____     Card 4: _____

Card 2: _____     Card 5: _____

Card 3: _____     Card 6: _____

Card 7: _____

*My question:* _____

_____

_____

*The first thing I observed about the cards I chose:*_____

_____

_____

_____

*My thoughts about this reading:* _____

_____

_____

_____

_____

_____

_____

_____

_____

_____

_____

_____

_____

_____

_____

_____

_____

_____

_____

_____

_____

_____

_____

_____

_____

Date of Reading:_____

```
        ┌─────┐
        │     │
        │  7  │
        │     │
        └─────┘

┌─────┐ ┌─────┐ ┌─────┐
│     │ │     │ │     │
│  5  │ │  1  │ │  3  │
│     │ │     │ │     │
└─────┘ └─────┘ └─────┘

┌─────┐ ┌─────┐ ┌─────┐
│     │ │     │ │     │
│  6  │ │  2  │ │  4  │
│     │ │     │ │     │
└─────┘ └─────┘ └─────┘
```

Card 1:_____        Card 4:_____

Card 2:_____        Card 5:_____

Card 3:_____        Card 6:_____

Card 7:_____

*My question:* _____

_____

_____

*The first thing I observed about the cards I chose:*_____

_____

_____

_____

*My thoughts about this reading:* _____

_____

_____

_____

_____

_____

_____

_____

_____

_____

_____

_____

_____

_____

_____

_____

_____

_____

_____

_____

_____

_____

_____

_____

_____

_____

_____

# THE BEGINNINGS TREE

THE BEGINNINGS TREE TAROT SPREAD is great for times when important life changes are under consideration: moving to a new home, beginning a new job, starting a major project. It is unusual from most tarot spreads in that the major and minor arcanas are separated. By dividing the arcanas, it is easier to examine the deeper issues underlying the situation undistracted by superficial details.

The first step in creating the Beginnings Tree layout is to separate the major and minor arcanas. Once you have two piles—one bearing only major arcana cards, the other only minor arcana—shuffle each one, concentrating on your new venture as you do so. When you are ready, choose four cards from each pile. Cards one to four are major arcana cards; cards five to eight are minor arcana cards. Then take the remaining cards (they should still be in two piles) and shuffle them together to choose one card; this is card nine. Place these nine cards as shown in the diagram:

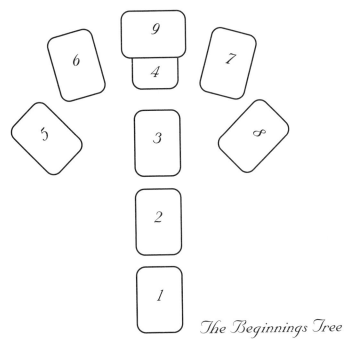

*The Beginnings Tree*

Card 1: The root of the venture. The deep issues pushing you toward it.
Card 2: Early growth of the venture. How your talents and actions will support it.
Card 3: The flowering of the venture. How others will react to it.
Card 4: The fruition of the venture. How it will change you and your life.
Cards 5 and 6: Details from your past to consider before you begin your venture.
Card 7 and 8: Details that will arise as the venture develops.
Card 9: The overall outcome. What can be expected if the venture begins as planned at this time.

Date of Reading:_____

```
        6        9              7
                 4

                 3          8
    5

                 2
```

Card 1:_____          Card 6:_____

Card 2:_____          Card 7:_____

Card 3:_____          Card 8:_____

Card 4:_____          Card 9:_____

Card 5:_____

```
                 1
```

*My question:* _____

_____

_____

*The first thing I observed about the cards I chose:*_____

_____

_____

_____

_____

*My thoughts about this reading:* _____

_____

_____

_____

_____

_____

_____

_____

_____

_____

_____

_____

_____

_____

_____

_____

_____

_____

_____

_____

_____

_____

_____

_____

_____

Date of Reading:_____

Card 1:_____

Card 2:_____

Card 3:_____

Card 4:_____

Card 5:_____

Card 6:_____

Card 7:_____

Card 8:_____

Card 9:_____

*My question:* _____

_____

_____

*The first thing I observed about the cards I chose:*_____

_____

_____

_____

_____

*My thoughts about this reading:* _____

_____

_____

_____

_____

_____

_____

_____

_____

_____

_____

_____

_____

_____

_____

_____

_____

_____

_____

_____

_____

_____

_____

_____

Date of Reading:_____

*9*

*4*

*6*

*7*

*3*

*5*

*8*

*2*

Card 1:_____

Card 2:_____

Card 3:_____

Card 4:_____

Card 5:_____

*1*

Card 6:_____

Card 7:_____

Card 8:_____

Card 9:_____

*My question:* _____

_____

_____

*The first thing I observed about the cards I chose:*_____

_____

_____

_____

_____

*My thoughts about this reading:* _____

_____

_____

_____

_____

_____

_____

_____

_____

_____

_____

_____

_____

_____

_____

_____

_____

_____

_____

_____

_____

_____

_____

_____

_____

_____

Date of Reading:_____

9

4

6

7

3

5

8

2

Card 1:_____      Card 6:_____

Card 2:_____      Card 7:_____

Card 3:_____      Card 8:_____

Card 4:_____      Card 9:_____

Card 5:_____

1

*My question:* _____

_____

_____

*The first thing I observed about the cards I chose:*_____

_____

_____

_____

_____

*My thoughts about this reading:* _____

_____

_____

_____

_____

_____

_____

_____

_____

_____

_____

_____

_____

_____

_____

_____

_____

_____

_____

_____

_____

_____

_____

_____

_____

_____

_____

_____

Date of Reading:_____

9

4

6          7

3

5          8

2

Card 1:_____        Card 6:_____

Card 2:_____        Card 7:_____

Card 3:_____        Card 8:_____

Card 4:_____        Card 9:_____

Card 5:_____

1

*My question:* _____

_____

_____

*The first thing I observed about the cards I chose:*_____

_____

_____

_____

_____

*My thoughts about this reading:* _____

_____

_____

_____

_____

_____

_____

_____

_____

_____

_____

_____

_____

_____

_____

_____

_____

_____

_____

_____

_____

_____

_____

_____

_____

# THE CELTIC CROSS

PERHAPS BECAUSE OF ITS VERSATILE ability to cover many aspects of a situation in great depth, the Celtic Cross is a staple of tarot spreads. For this reading, give yourself at least twenty minutes.

The first step in creating the Celtic Cross is to choose a card from the deck to signify yourself. There are several ways to do this. Traditional ways include selecting a court card—prince, princess, king or queen—according to the age, sex and coloring of the querant; for example, a young woman with light hair would be represented by the Princess of Cups, an older man with red hair, the King of Staves.

Another way to choose the significator is to choose the major arcana card associated with a goddess affiliated with the matter being examined. For example, you could use the goddess Venus, as represented in the Love card (number VI), for queries regarding romantic relationships; use the goddess Tara (Beginnings, number 0) if your question is about starting a new business.

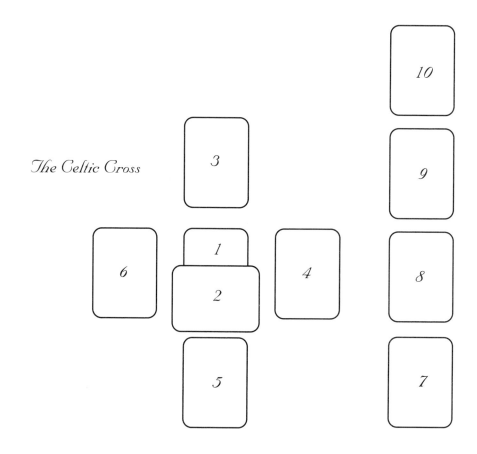

*The Celtic Cross*

After the significator card is decided upon, the deck is shuffled, cut and ten cards are chosen from the top. They are placed in order of appearance as shown in the diagram, with the significator beneath card #1:

Each card in the Celtic Cross Spread represents one area of the question or issue being examined in the reading.

*Card 1:* The overall situation, or atmosphere, surrounding you in regards to the question.

*Card 2:* What is influencing the situation for better or for worse. What needs to be considered.

*Card 3:* The foundation of the issue.

*Card 4:* The past, or influence that is now passing away.

*Card 5:* What is on your mind at this time.

*Card 6:* Near future, or the influence now coming into play.

*Card 7:* How you see the situation, or how it is influencing you at this time.

*Card 8:* How others view you in this situation; ways they may help or hinder.

*Card 9:* Hopes and fears; the emotions surrounding you when you consider the situation at hand.

*Card 10:* Possible outcome, if things continue on the path now taken. Remember, this card is a reflection of the current moment in time; it can change depending upon the course of action taken.

Date of Reading:_____

10

3

1

2

6

4

8

5

7

9

Significator Card: _____

Card 1:_____          Card 6: _____

Card 2:_____          Card 7: _____

Card 3:_____          Card 8: _____

Card 4:_____          Card 9: _____

Card 5:_____          Card 10:_____

*My question:* _____

_____

_____

*The first thing I observed about the cards I chose:*_____

_____

_____

*My thoughts about this reading:* _____

_____

_____

_____

_____

_____

_____

_____

_____

_____

_____

_____

_____

_____

_____

_____

_____

_____

_____

_____

_____

_____

_____

_____

_____

_____

_____

_____

Date of Reading:_____

```
                                                    ┌─────────┐
                                                    │         │
                                                    │   10    │
                                                    │         │
                                                    └─────────┘

           ┌─────────┐                              ┌─────────┐
           │         │                              │         │
           │    3    │                              │    9    │
           │         │                              │         │
           └─────────┘                              └─────────┘

  ┌───────┐   ┌──────┐   ┌───────┐                  ┌─────────┐
  │       │   │  1   │   │       │                  │         │
  │   6   │  ┌┴──────┴┐  │   4   │                  │    8    │
  │       │  │   2    │  │       │                  │         │
  └───────┘  └────────┘  └───────┘                  └─────────┘

           ┌─────────┐                              ┌─────────┐
           │         │                              │         │
           │    5    │                              │    7    │
           │         │                              │         │
           └─────────┘                              └─────────┘
```

Significator Card: _____

Card 1:_____     Card 6: _____

Card 2:_____     Card 7: _____

Card 3:_____     Card 8: _____

Card 4:_____     Card 9: _____

Card 5:_____     Card 10:_____

*My question:* _____

_____

_____


*The first thing I observed about the cards I chose:*_____

_____

_____

*My thoughts about this reading:*_____

_____

_____

_____

_____

_____

_____

_____

_____

_____

_____

_____

_____

_____

_____

_____

_____

_____

_____

_____

_____

_____

_____

_____

Date of Reading:_____

```
                                                    ┌────────┐
                                                    │        │
                                                    │   10   │
                                                    │        │
                                                    └────────┘

        ┌────────┐                                  ┌────────┐
        │        │                                  │        │
        │   3    │                                  │   9    │
        │        │                                  │        │
        └────────┘                                  └────────┘

┌────────┐   ┌────────┐   ┌────────┐   ┌────────┐
│        │   │   1    │   │        │   │        │
│   6    │   ├────────┤   │   4    │   │   8    │
│        │   │   2    │   │        │   │        │
└────────┘   └────────┘   └────────┘   └────────┘

        ┌────────┐                                  ┌────────┐
        │        │                                  │        │
        │   5    │                                  │   7    │
        │        │                                  │        │
        └────────┘                                  └────────┘
```

Significator Card: _____

Card 1:_____        Card 6: _____

Card 2:_____        Card 7: _____

Card 3:_____        Card 8: _____

Card 4:_____        Card 9: _____

Card 5:_____        Card 10:_____

*My question:* _____

_____

_____


*The first thing I observed about the cards I chose:*_____

_____

_____

*My thoughts about this reading:*_____

_____

_____

_____

_____

_____

_____

_____

_____

_____

_____

_____

_____

_____

_____

_____

_____

_____

_____

_____

_____

_____

_____

_____

_____

_____

_____

_____

Date of Reading:_____

```
                                                    ┌────────┐
                                                    │        │
                                                    │   10   │
                                                    │        │
                                                    └────────┘
        ┌────────┐                                  ┌────────┐
        │        │                                  │        │
        │   3    │                                  │   9    │
        │        │                                  │        │
        └────────┘                                  └────────┘
┌────────┐  ┌──────┐  ┌────────┐          ┌────────┐
│        │  │  1   │  │        │          │        │
│   6    │ ┌┴──────┴┐ │   4    │          │   8    │
│        │ │   2    │ │        │          │        │
└────────┘ └────────┘ └────────┘          └────────┘
        ┌────────┐                                  ┌────────┐
        │        │                                  │        │
        │   5    │                                  │   7    │
        │        │                                  │        │
        └────────┘                                  └────────┘
```

Significator Card: _____

Card 1:_____        Card 6: _____

Card 2:_____        Card 7: _____

Card 3:_____        Card 8: _____

Card 4:_____        Card 9: _____

Card 5:_____        Card 10:_____

*My question:* _____

_____

_____

*The first thing I observed about the cards I chose:*_____

_____

_____

*My thoughts about this reading:*_____

_____

_____

_____

_____

_____

_____

_____

_____

_____

_____

_____

_____

_____

_____

_____

_____

_____

_____

_____

_____

_____

_____

_____

_____

_____

Date of Reading:_____

| | | | 10 |
| 3 | | | 9 |
| | 1 | | |
| 6 | 2 | 4 | 8 |
| | 5 | | 7 |

Significator Card: _____

Card 1:_____        Card 6: _____

Card 2:_____        Card 7: _____

Card 3:_____        Card 8: _____

Card 4:_____        Card 9: _____

Card 5:_____        Card 10:_____

*My question:* _____

_____

_____

*The first thing I observed about the cards I chose:*_____

_____

_____

*My thoughts about this reading:* _____

_____

_____

_____

_____

_____

_____

_____

_____

_____

_____

_____

_____

_____

_____

_____

_____

_____

_____

_____

_____

_____

_____

_____

_____

_____

_____

_____

_____

# THE RELATIONSHIP CROSS

THIS TAROT SPREAD, TAUGHT TO me by tarot reader Melanie Hope Greenberg, is valuable for exploring complex questions where only two people are involved. What is especially good about the Relationship Cross is that three cards are used to sum up each area explored, allowing a more complete picture than can be created with a single card.

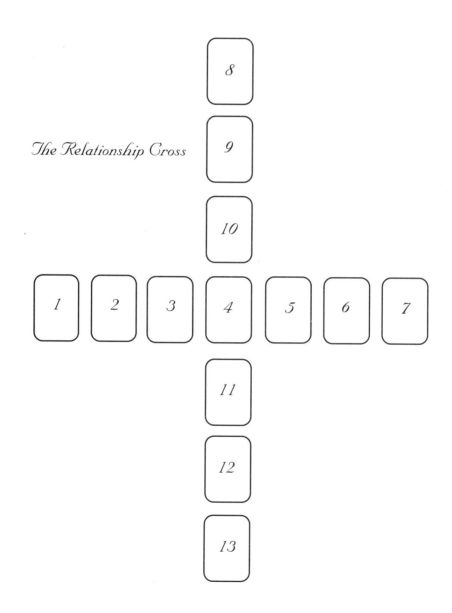

*The Relationship Cross*

This spread is also unusual because of the order in which the cards are examined; instead of reading from the first card chosen to the last, cards are read according to group positions. Allow yourself a minimum of thirty minutes to explore the multi-faceted aspects of this spread. After shuffling and cutting the deck, choose thirteen cards from the top. Place them as in the diagram shown at left.

When reading this spread, first examine cards 13 though 11, which represents the relationship's past. Then move onto cards 1 though 3, or the relationship's present. Next look at cards 5 through 7, which represents the other person in the situation. Cards 8 through 10 show the future as it may appear according to the way things are now being played out. Finally, card 4 should be considered for an overview of the reading.

> *Cards 1 through 3:* These cards represent you and your present role in the relationship being examined.
> *Card 4:* Represents the outcome of the question regarding the relationship.
> *Cards 5 through 7:* These cards represent the other person involved in the relationship and their current situation.
> *Cards 8 through 10:* The future of the relationship, if things continue as they are.
> *Cards 11 through 13:* The past or history of the relationship and how it has affected the present situation.

Date of Reading: 7-18-05

| | |
|---|---|
| | 8 |
| | 9 |
| | 10 |

| 1 | 2 | 3 | 4 | 5 | 6 | 7 |
|---|---|---|---|---|---|---|

11

Card 1: XVI Oppression

Card 2: III Fertility

Card 3: XII Sacrifice

Card 4: 4 Staves

Card 5: IV Power

Card 6: Prince Swords

Card 7: 4 Pentacles

Card 8: 5 cups

Card 9: O - Beginnings

Card 10: 4 - cups

Card 11: King Staves

Card 12: XI Strength

Card 13: 5 Swords

12

13

*My question:* _____

_____

_____

*The first thing I observed about the cards I chose:*_____

_____

_____

_____

*My thoughts about this reading:*_____

_____

_____

_____

_____

_____

_____

_____

_____

_____

_____

_____

_____

_____

_____

_____

_____

_____

Date of Reading:_____

8

9

10

| 1 | 2 | 3 | 4 | 5 | 6 | 7 |

Card 1:_____

11

Card 8:_____

Card 2:_____

Card 9:_____

Card 3:_____

Card 10:_____

12

Card 4:_____

Card 11:_____

Card 5:_____

Card 12:_____

Card 6:_____

Card 13:_____

Card 7:_____

13

*My question:*_____

_____

_____

*The first thing I observed about the cards I chose:*_____

_____

_____

_____


*My thoughts about this reading:*_____

_____

_____

_____

_____

_____

_____

_____

_____

_____

_____

_____

_____

_____

_____

_____

_____

_____

_____

_____

Date of Reading:_____

| | | | 8 | | | |

| | | | 9 | | | |

| | | | 10 | | | |

| 1 | 2 | 3 | 4 | 5 | 6 | |

| | | | 11 | | | |

| | | | 12 | | | |

| | | | 13 | | | |

Card 1:_____

Card 2:_____

Card 3:_____

Card 4:_____

Card 5:_____

Card 6:_____

Card 7:_____

Card 8:_____

Card 9:_____

Card 10:_____

Card 11:_____

Card 12:_____

Card 13:_____

*My question:*_____

_____

_____

*The first thing I observed about the cards I chose:* _____

_____

_____

_____


*My thoughts about this reading:* _____

_____

_____

_____

_____

_____

_____

_____

_____

_____

_____

_____

_____

_____

_____

_____

_____

_____

_____

_____

_____

Date of Reading:_____

8

9

10

| 1 | 2 | 3 | 4 | 5 | 6 | 7 |

11

Card 1: _____

Card 2: _____

Card 3: _____

Card 4: _____

Card 5: _____

Card 6: _____

Card 7: _____

12

Card 8: _____

Card 9: _____

Card 10:_____

Card 11:_____

Card 12:_____

Card 13:_____

13

*My question:*_____

_____

_____

*The first thing I observed about the cards I chose:*____

_____

_____

_____


*My thoughts about this reading:*_____

_____

_____

_____

_____

_____

_____

_____

_____

_____

_____

_____

_____

_____

_____

_____

_____

_____

_____

Date of Reading:_____

| | |
|---|---|
| | *8* |
| | *9* |
| | *10* |

| | | | | | | |
|---|---|---|---|---|---|---|
| *1* | *2* | *3* | *4* | *5* | *6* | *7* |

*11*

*12*

*13*

Card 1:_____

Card 2:_____

Card 3:_____

Card 4:_____

Card 5:_____

Card 6:_____

Card 7:_____

Card 8:_____

Card 9:_____

Card 10:_____

Card 11:_____

Card 12:_____

Card 13:_____

*My question:*_____

_____

_____

*The first thing I observed about the cards I chose:* _____

_____

_____

_____


*My thoughts about this reading:* _____

_____

_____

_____

_____

_____

_____

_____

_____

_____

_____

_____

_____

_____

_____

_____

_____

_____

_____

_____

_____

_____

_____

# THE CIRCLE OF STRENGTH

THE CIRCLE OF STRENGTH is especially useful for complex questions where one's patience and strength may be tested. The circular layout of this tarot spread reminds us of the cycle of life —what is unbearable now will change if we can endure it long enough.

Unlike other the tarot spreads in this book, the Circle of Strength was created to systematically examine a situation as it unfolds in time: twelve cards symbolize the twelve months of the year, with three cards for each of the four seasons of the year. As in the Relationship Cross, these three cards are examined together as one unit to gain a fuller picture of each passing phase.

Take a moment to concentrate on your situation at hand. Then shuffle the cards, cut the deck and choose fifteen cards from the top. Lay them out as shown in the diagram. As you read, begin from Card 1 and move out clockwise:

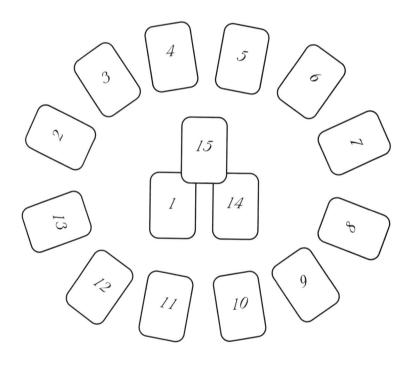

*The Circle of Strength*

*Card 1:* This card represents beginning of the cycle, or where you stand now in regard to the situation begin examined in the reading.

*Cards 2 through 4:* These three cards represent the first season of the cycle, or the beginnings of it.

*Cards 5 through 7:* These cards represent the second season of the cycle, or the development.

*Cards 8 through 10:* These cards represent the third season of the cycle, or the unfolding.

*Cards 11 through 13:* These cards represent the final season of the cycle, or the resolution of this situation.

*Card 14:* This card offers a possible conclusion to your situation, taking into consideration all that may come to pass if things continue as they now stand.

*Card 15:* The final card of this tarot spread presents an overall theme for the reading. Consider this card a valuable guide to what may strengthen you as you undergo all the trials and triumphs of this time.

Date of Reading:_____

Card 1:_____

Card 2:_____

Card 3:_____

Card 4:_____

Card 5:_____

Card 6:_____

Card 7:_____

Card 8:_____

Card 9:_____

Card 10:_____

Card 11:_____

Card 12:_____

Card 13:_____

Card 14:_____

Card 15:_____

*My question:*_____

_____

_____

*The first thing I observed about the cards I chose:* _____

_____

_____

_____


*My thoughts about this reading:* _____

_____

_____

_____

_____

_____

_____

_____

_____

_____

_____

_____

_____

_____

_____

_____

_____

_____

_____

_____

_____

_____

Date of Reading:_____

4

5

3

6

2

7

15

1    14

13

8

12

9

11    10

Card 1:_____

Card 2:_____

Card 3:_____

Card 4:_____

Card 5:_____

Card 6:_____

Card 7:_____

Card 8:_____

Card 9:_____

Card 10:_____

Card 11:_____

Card 12:_____

Card 13:_____

Card 14:_____

Card 15: _____

*My question:*_____

_____

_____

*The first thing I observed about the cards I chose:* _____

_____

_____

_____


*My thoughts about this reading:* _____

_____

_____

_____

_____

_____

_____

_____

_____

_____

_____

_____

_____

_____

_____

_____

_____

_____

_____

_____

_____

Date of Reading:_____

4

5

3

6

2

15

7

1   14

13

8

12

9

11   10

Card 1:_____

Card 2:_____

Card 3:_____

Card 4:_____

Card 5:_____

Card 6:_____

Card 7:_____

Card 8:_____

Card 9:_____

Card 10:_____

Card 11:_____

Card 12:_____

Card 13:_____

Card 14:_____

Card 15:_____

*My question:*_____

_____

_____

*The first thing I observed about the cards I chose:* _____

_____

_____

_____

*My thoughts about this reading:* _____

_____

_____

_____

_____

_____

_____

_____

_____

_____

_____

_____

_____

_____

_____

_____

_____

_____

_____

_____

_____

Date of Reading:_____

Card layout:
- 4
- 5
- 3
- 6
- 2
- 7
- 15
- 13
- 1
- 14
- 8
- 12
- 11
- 10
- 9

Card 1: _____

Card 2: _____

Card 3: _____

Card 4: _____

Card 5: _____

Card 6: _____

Card 7: _____

Card 8: _____

Card 9: _____

Card 10:_____

Card 11:_____

Card 12:_____

Card 13:_____

Card 14:_____

Card 15: _____

*My question:*_____

_____

_____

*The first thing I observed about the cards I chose:* _____

_____

_____

_____


*My thoughts about this reading:* _____

_____

_____

_____

_____

_____

_____

_____

_____

_____

_____

_____

_____

_____

_____

_____

_____

_____

_____

_____

Date of Reading: ____________

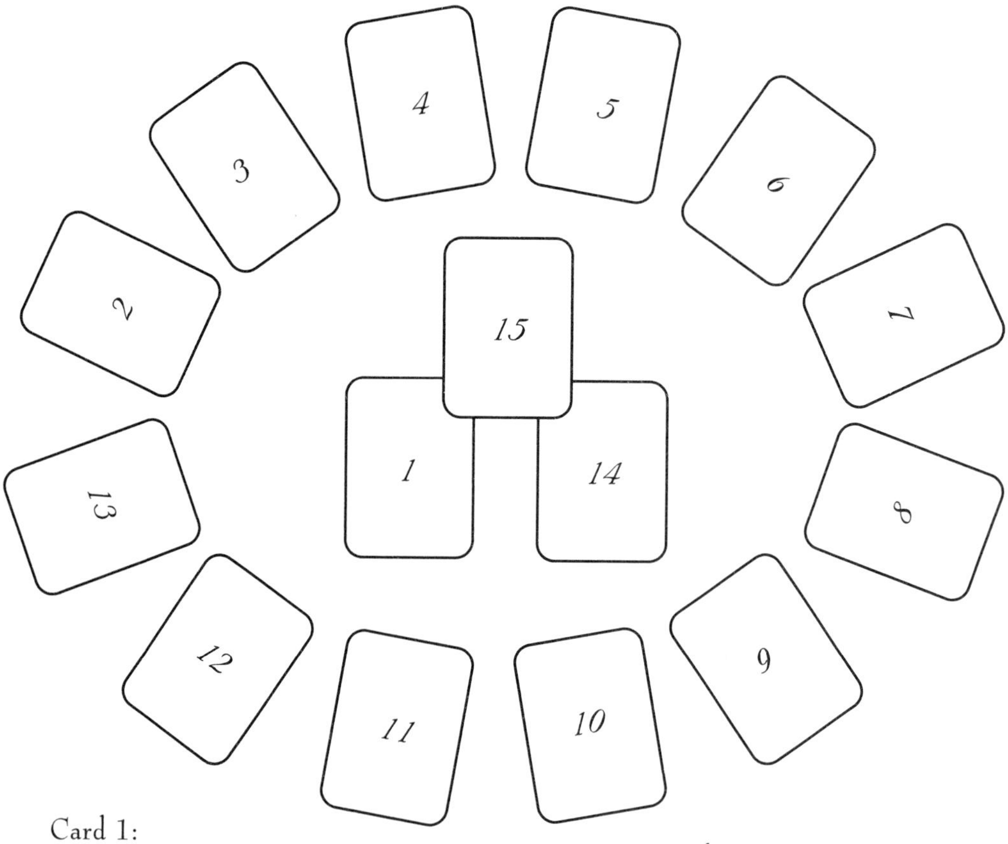


Card 1: ____________

Card 2: ____________

Card 3: ____________

Card 4: ____________

Card 5: ____________

Card 6: ____________

Card 7: ____________

Card 8: ____________

Card 9: ____________

Card 10: ____________

Card 11: ____________

Card 12: ____________

Card 13: ____________

Card 14: ____________

Card 15: ____________

*My question:* ________________________________________

________________________________________

________________________________________

*The first thing I observed about the cards I chose:*_____

_____

_____

_____


*My thoughts about this reading:*_____

_____

_____

_____

_____

_____

_____

_____

_____

_____

_____

_____

_____

_____

_____

_____

_____

_____

_____

_____

# RESOURCES

Like any tool, mastering the tarot is a journey that takes time, study and thought; hopefully, *The Goddess Tarot* will whet your interest to continue learning about the tarot and goddesses. What follows is a list of resources I found useful as I worked on *The Goddess Tarot* and *The Goddess Tarot Workbook* or that I thought might be of interest.

## *Books*

So many wonderful books are available about the tarot and goddesses that it is impossible to list them all; perhaps these can serve as an introduction. For those of you who would like to learn more about goddesses, a more extensive bibliography can also be found in my book *The Book of Goddesses*:

Ann, Martha and Dorothy Myers Imel. *Goddesses in World Mythology.* Oxford University Press, 1993.

Baring, Anne and Jules Cashford. *The Myth of the Goddess.* Viking Books, 1992.

Gearhart, Sally and Susan Rennie. *A Feminist Tarot.* Alyson Publications, 1997.

Greer, Mary K. *Tarot for Your Self; A Workbook for Personal Transformation.* Newcastle Publishing Co., Inc., 1984.

Larrington, Carolyne, editor. *The Feminist Companion to Mythology.* Pandora/Harper Collins, 1992.

Monaghan, Patricia. *The Book of Goddesses and Heroines.* Llewellyn Publications, 1993.

Palmer, Helen (introduction), Signe E. Echols, M. S., Robert Mueller, Ph.D. and Sandra A. Thomson. *Spiritual Tarot: Seventy-Eight Paths to Personal Development.* Avon Books, New York, 1996.

Shavick, Nancy. *The Tarot.* Berkley Publishing Group, 1988.

Stone, Merlin. *When God Was a Woman.* Harvest/Harcourt Brace Jovanovich Books, 1976.

Stuart, Micheline. *The Tarot Path to Self-Development*. Shambhala Publications, 1996.

Walker, Barbara C. *The Woman's Encyclopedia of Myths and Secrets*. Harper San Francisco, 1983.

✧ ✧ ✧

# *Internet*

What follows are some websites pertaining to the tarot. Bear in mind that the nature of the world wide web is ever changing, ever fluid; these addresses were accurate at press time:

*www.aeclectic.net/tarot*. Aeclectic Tarot is an all encompassing exploration of the diversity and beauty of the tarot. Featuring art from more than 200 different tarot oracle and divination decks.

*www.ata-tarot.com*. The official website for the American Tarot Association. The ATA is organized for the purpose of bringing together qualified students and teachers of the Tarot who are willing to subscribe to a high ethical standard.

*www.atasteoftarot.com*. The website of Laura Mead Desmit, a professional tarot reader. Desmit originated the Burning Question, a tarot spread featured in this workbook.

*www.goddesstarot.com*. The official *Goddess Tarot* website. Offering information about *The Goddess Tarot*, free online oracle readings and much more.

*www.learntarot.org*. Joan Bunning, author of *Learning the Tarot*, offers an online course on how to use the tarot. Bunning believes that the tarot can help you understand yourself better and teach you how to tap your inner resources more confidently. These lessons are geared toward beginners, but experienced tarot users will find some useful ideas here too.

*www.usgamesinc.com*. The publisher of *The Goddess Tarot*. A rich resource of tarot decks, books and other related merchandise.

# INDEX